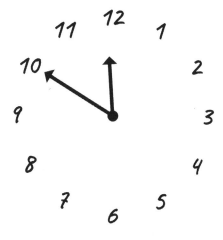

Kit Lindfield is a psychotherapist practising in London

Time's Up In Shrinksville

A 20th Century Tale of Love & Substances

& Shrinks & Their Kids

Kit Lindfield

Published by Lindfield Ink

Copyright © Kit Lindfield 2017

This book is based on the author's experiences. Some names,
identifying characteristics, dialogue & details have been
changed, reconstructed or fictionalised.

A catalogue record for this book is
available from the British Library.

ISBN 978-1-5272-1407-1

Typeset by EF Designs

For the Lindfield family, for all the kids who grew up in psychotherapist households & in memory of my parents

Foreword

This is mostly a true story in the subjective sense, along with some name changes and a few truncated timelines and narrative devices (of course). The way it felt as a young person growing up in a mid 20th century, liberal, psychoanalytical family was my initial intention in the writing of this and is, I hope, an accurate enough portrayal recognisable to others of a similar background should they happen to come across this.

Several unexpected themes emerged which turned out to hold just as much energy for me as the initial idea, such as the theme of substance use and abuse, prescription and recreational; crises of identity, sexual, spiritual and otherwise, figure too - the secret lives and passions that were lived out in parallel to the tenuous family myth we upheld. Fundamentally I discovered, it is a story about people and love in its presence and absence.

The only character who may not quite exist in real life is dear Dr Sebastian Maelstrum (who evolved to tell the story).

I do not mean to offend anyone or any institution though I cannot guarantee that this will be the case.

Part One

_____

The Beginning...

London, January 2017

Hi Dr Maelstrum
I've been given your email by a colleague. I'm a therapist wanting to go back into therapy myself for a bit. Could you please let me know if and when you can see me and also where you practice from?

Thanks v much
Kit Lindfield

- - - - - - - - - - - - - - -

Hello Kit
Thank you for being in touch. I will shortly have an evening space coming up in my north London practice.

Before we meet would you write a short biography, including the important turning points and any significant events that spring to mind and something about your family background. Please then forward it to me ahead of our first meeting.

Thank you and I look forward to hearing back from you.

Kind regards, Dr. S. Maelstrum

- - - - - - - - - - - - - -

Hi Dr Maestrum
My father was a Freudian shrink, my mother was a doctor. I'm the only girl, middle child of 3. All the usual things happened - dysfunctional relationships, single parenthood, numerous neurosis and existential crises. I got knocked down by a Morris Minor when I was 17.

Could you please let me know if and when I can make an appointment to see you?

Thanks v much
Best, Kit Lindfield

- - - - - - - - - - - - - -

Hello Kit
Thank you for sending your very short biography and the few scant details about your background. It would significantly benefit our work together if you could kindly write a little more. Perhaps a couple of A4 sheets so you can elaborate on the start you have made. A bit more about family relationships would be helpful. Once completed we can then schedule in a first meeting.

Kind Regards, Dr Maelstrum

Hi Dr Maelstrum
This is not at all what I was expecting when I emailed you. But ok I will give it a go and get back to you when I've done it.
Best,
Kit

Ps is this writing thing really necessary? None of my other shrinks have ever asked for this!

Alright Then.....

When I was 3 and a half and my big brother Sam (also an April baby) was almost exactly a year older, we lived in a ground floor flat just behind what is now the Camden Arts Centre in Hampstead. The family had recently returned by Union Castle ship from an 18 month stint in South Africa. My father, Ezra, had unsuccessfully tried to launch a psychoanalytical practice back in Cape Town where he and my mother, Marion, had grown up; that is after he had completed his training in London in the early 1950's with Anna Freud. In fact, London in the 1950's had been the birthplace of my older brother and myself.

We settled back into the familiarity of our former north London existence as if we had never been away, blotting out the impact of this trip to the southern hemisphere as best we could. Being just a small kid and locked into a ferocious rivalry with my brother Sam, I had no idea what had gone on and it would be years before I did.

Whatever they say about explicit memory I have early technicolor South African snapshots in my mind from around my second and third years: the unnaturally fine, white Capetonian sand; the alien translucent 'bluebottles' on the beach which were in fact stranded jellyfish; the coloured strings of lightbulbs lining the promenade; the gardener who told me I would go to jail if I picked the roses in the sloping garden at Bridge End. And then the journey home on the Union Castle liner where with fat childproofed needles I sewed my Minnie Mouse cards each morning in the nursery, keeping my head down, terrified that I would be picked on to be chucked into the upper deck swimming pool as we crossed the equator (a nasty threatening ritual when you are only 3 and a bit and cannot yet swim). At some point on the journey home I dressed up as an orange whilst my older, yet noticeably smaller brother was the lemon, my mother having slavishly crafted our costumes out of crepe paper, staples, cardboard and sellotape. What were we thinking? There is a photo of us where we look quite bizarre as the confused and uncomfortable Orange and the bewildered bad tempered Lemon. (I remember absolutely nothing about my father on that journey - I guess he must have been otherwise engaged and not in the least interested in fancy dress, equatorial rituals or Minnie Mouse.)

My mother always reminded us that the outbound journey from Southampton to Cape Town had been far worse on an ancient rusting banana boat ie a cargo ship, that had creaked and groaned its way slowly down south in stormy unrelentingly crappy weather. I would ask my mother 'Did we stop off anywhere else in Africa?' She would reply 'Only briefly in Kenya and Tanganyika' which sounded supremely exotic to my uneducated ears. I would boast back at nursery school in London 'I've been to Kaneeyia and Tangranyeeka!' from then on, omitting the 'briefly' bit.

Here though, safely back on dry land in Hampstead we negotiated our tiny, black-and-white tiled, ground floor space with each other, our new au pair, our white long haired cat Bimbo, a tabby stray we named Kitalena, and my father's analytical practice. The tangerine walled lounge became his waiting room during working hours, but being at the very opposite end of the flat to his consulting room, us not bumping into the patient along the long narrow corridor, and more importantly the patient not bumping into any family members at all, ever, became the prime consideration.

When it wasn't being used by the waiting patient, the scruffy green sofa in the lounge became our refuge: Something to hide behind when "Pathfinders to Venus and Mars" - supposedly a kids' TV programme - scared us witless; its tatty, sagging cushions giving us something to stick our feet up on to avoid them being trampled when our parents did their jive practice courtesy of Duke Ellington and Dave Brubeck.

During working hours - which often extended from first thing in the morning until way past our official bedtime - we were taught the invaluable art of 'creeping around'. Every analyst's child knows about this one, if the parent works from home. We learned the art too of becoming 'invisible' and failed invariably in our attempts to become 'inaudible'. We were just kids and very busily engrossed in the business of squabbling endlessly with each other. Most of the time we lived in the steamy kitchen, huddled together in its cosy intimate space with our eggs on toast and did our best to avoid venturing into any other part of the flat whilst Dad worked. The bedroom I shared with Sam was just next to the lounge/waiting room and therefore pretty close in proximity to the super sensitive ears and eyes of the ever curious patient. They heard us and we heard them, but we all pretended not to.

The saving grace was the ramshackle, semi wild garden sloping all the way down, the distance of the entire block, to the main road below. It was a rubble strewn untamed space to run around in and lose ourselves. Somewhere to let off steam and release the frustrations of having to be so damn quiet and discrete the rest of the time. And we did.

It didn't take too long before we outgrew the confines of this small flat - we couldn't contain ourselves and it couldn't contain us. We were bursting at the seams, especially my mother who was heavily pregnant with our younger brother. I was 6 when we moved into the big house and Jake was born.

Lessons in Hygiene with Ezra

There was always something a little subversive about my dear Dad. One day, when I was about 4 he taught me (apparently under the explicit instructions of my mother) how to clean out the bathtub after using it. He explained there were 2 Methods I could apply:

Method No. One: You take the cleaning fluid and the scourer and you scrub away vigorously at the scummy 'ring' you have created with your bodily detritis. Then you rinse. Fair enough - we only bathed about once a week. We were filthy kids. This was the conventional method and the one my mother undoubtedly wanted us to learn.

Method No. Two: Alternatively, you fill the bath so full no one will ever look for a scummy ring so high up the side of the bath. You therefore do not have to clean out the bath at all. Naturally this is the method my father recommended.

Years later on holiday in France I remember my father distressed and haranguing my mother. She was cleaning the bath, vigorously, using Method Number One. I overheard his frantic words to her:

"For Christ sake sake stop this Marion, please, **please** stop! You'll make yourself sick again if you carry on like this!"

She did and she did, but that all happened some years later.

English Lessons with Marion

At around the same time as the bath cleaning lessons, my mother was taking it in turns with our upstairs neighbour to do the school run with us. By 'us' I mean me and our neighbours' daughter, 'Tiny'. Tiny and I went to the same progressive nursery school in North End Road.

That I was now going to a progressive nursery school was in itself progress. I had started off going to a place called the House on the Hill which according to my parents, it turned out, was being run by '*psychopathic and sadistic nurses*'. Sam and I were whipped out of this school mid term when the aforementioned nurses were caught in the act. I did in fact witness some pretty gruesome things. Like for example, one lunch time a little girl was forced to eat whilst she was actually physically being sick. Exiled off into the corner with her at a table for the 'naughty' kids, my punishment for dropping a dollop of spinach on the brand spanking new dining table, I tried to block out the sound of her retching. It's not that easy eating next to someone being sick into their dinner plate. And there were other public humiliations that my brother remembered involving trousers being unnecessarily pulled down and similar unsavoury occurrences. When anyone asked me why I had so suddenly left this delightful establishment I would reply '*because the nurses were sadists*'. I was only 4 but I think I was getting the gist and a handle on the terminology.

Back to the story: Tiny and I were just getting into the car to go to the new nursery school one morning in the usual haphazard, half asleep way that kids do, when my mother stepped in a huge pile of dog crap. "Oh fuck" she shouted "Fucking, fucking hell. Fuck this, fuck everything!" Mum was very upset, the closest to crying I had ever seen and clearly more upset than a bit of dog poo warranted. I was mystified, "Mummy what does 'fuck' mean?" She replied "It's a Very Bad Word and you must promise me you will never, ever say it, Never Ever, not to anyone!" "Ok Mummy, I promise, I promise." For a very long time I got confused by the word fuck and its similarity to the word muck and then 'yuck' slipped into the mix. Fuck became synonymous with the image of dog muck in my developing brain and much as I tried to put a new spin on it, it never really shifted. I did break my promise though.

Tiny's mother was in a state. Tiny's father was a racing driver and it seems the marriage had hit the buffers. He had disappeared - raced off with someone else's wife, I later discovered. On the days when he delivered us to school we'd clamber into his low slung shiny sports car with the roof down and whizz off, but this time neither he nor his exotic car would be back. One afternoon after school I asked Tiny's mum " Where's he gone?" "Mind your own business, you horrible, nosey child!" she snapped viciously. I did mind my own business from then on. I shut up, shut my cake hole. I realised asking questions was getting me into trouble. There were a number of things I got very wrong and the list was growing. There were plenty of items now that could be filed under the heading 'Bad':

Bad nurses, bad dog, bad word, bad dad, but mostly **bad child for asking all the wrong questions.**

- - - - - - - - - - - - - - -

```
Hi Dr Maelstrum - I've written a bit more than you
asked for but I'm on a roll so I'll keep going -
hope this is ok with you?
Kit
```

Our New House

(and a new working arrangement)

Don't Come Knocking...

Our association with Tiny and her disintegrating family life came to an end when we moved. We were all incredibly proud of our new house. The story my father tells us is that when he first saw it it looked absolutely hideous and was painted a dark miserable wartime green. Another of its unbecoming features was the dangerously derelict, flooded bomb shelter at the back of the messy garden. But Ezra recognised a bargain when it was staring him in the face, and elbowed through the crowd of potential rival buyers to get his offer in first. He told the agent he'd take it then and there. It was dirt cheap and massive compared to what we were used to. It had six bedrooms on three floors. Beneath its superficial hideousness it was a beauty of a house - it only took a bit of paint to transform it. And that's how we ended up on the other side of Hampstead in a plane tree lined avenue backing onto the grounds and tennis courts of Westfield College.

Our new house had two huge parquet floored reception

rooms downstairs, one of which became my father's consulting room. It had double doors leading to the lounge which were closed nearly all the time, the lounge being completely out of bounds during consulting hours. The adjoining doors were only flung open on rare occasions for large scale 'entertaining'.

There was a small inconvenient problem with this working arrangement: This time round the waiting room for the patients had been constructed in the space immediately as you entered the house through the front door. From this waiting room there were two doors: one door into the very-private-and-out-of-bounds consulting room and another into the hall and the rest of the house. This meant that none of the family or any of our friends could use the front door when my father was working because we would bang straight into the fragile patient sitting in the waiting room. We were instructed to creep silently round the back of the house and to avoid, at all costs, coming up the front garden path at the same time as the patient. In fact, bizarrely, we would often walk straight past our own front gate and pretend not to live there if we spotted the patient en route.

As kids we knew it was terribly important to abide by these house rules and that under no circumstances was the ever protected patient to be exposed to "us". Why this might be the case remained unquestioned - it was simply how it was. In the early days our au pair would open the door to the patient. It was acceptable for some reason for her to be seen by them. Later, when buzzers and intercoms had been invented the patient would get buzzed in, or at least the person arriving on the doorstep at the same time as the next patient appointment would.

When I was in my early teens, one of our more edgy and slightly older friends, Phil, got accidentally buzzed in to find himself in the waiting room with the 2 closed doors. Bandana'ed Phil had an enormous scruffy rucksack on his back and was kitted out in filthy ripped denim that stank from weeks of hitching round Spain undeodorized. It's quite possible he might even have had a half smoked joint in his grimy, nicotine stained hand. Confused by the 2 doors and faced with the choice of which one to open, a bit like in the riddle, Phil and his rucksack chose to enter the sacred inner sanctum of the very-private-and-out-of-bounds consulting room. I can just about imagine the scene and the expression on my friend's face: my horrified father sitting in his leather chair, cigarette falling from his mouth, behind the poor patient lying innocently on the couch. And then Phil in all innocence too, uttering

"Hi Doc Ezra, man, I'm busting for a leak. Where's the nearest loo?"

Clearly something sensationally awful had been visited upon the professional life of my father and the traumatising silence in the house that evening over dinner said it all: Phil's unforgivable mistake had most likely set back the psychoanalytical process several valuable and expensive years. Us kids were naturally entirely responsible for it, as a very furious Ezra continued, in perpetuity, to remind us.

Strangely or perhaps not, a recurring dream throughout my life even as an adult has been about a 'violated consulting room'.

The dream has two variations: Either my father is in his consulting room but it's full of all the wrong and unacceptable things and people who really shouldn't be there (like Phil perhaps and various others); or, alternatively the same is occurring in my own therapy room at home. In these dreams the room is full of used bedsheets and sometimes the people who have just used them and I am frantically trying to get rid of them before the patient/client arrives. All that dirty laundry. What I wonder would old Dr Freud have thought?

Ants & Stars & the Pool of Spirits

"I don't want to achieve immortality through my work; I want to achieve immortality through not dying" - Woody Allen

Shortly after moving into our new house I began to have night terrors. They probably started around the time my mother lost her own mother, Rose, sometime during my 6th year. I think they, the night terrors, had been brewing for a while. It started with my gazing into the night sky as a very young kid as far back in time as I can remember. I saw the endless darkness and then the thousands of tiny stars accompanied by the thoughts that went through my head. "Can this go on forever? Where am *I* in all of this? What happens at the end of the universe? Is there a wall? No of course not, you idiot!" went the inner voice. My own smallness and insignificance scared me. I was infinitesimally insignificant - and I mattered less than a tiny microscopic particle of dust.

Conversely, during our stay in South Africa when I was 2 or 3 years old, something happened to me at bath time one evening. I was watching as some tiny ants wandered round the edge of the bathtub. Something about the bigness of me, the smallness of them and their swarming nature tapped into the neural circuits, triggering some kind of ancient fight/flight response. I became hysterical. It was at this exact point, according to my mother's own recollections, that the contented, always smiling, easy-going kid began to disappear. It wasn't right that I could so easily squish the life out of ant, just as life could and would inevitably, at some point, be squished out of me too.

Night terrors in the classical sense are like having a major panic attack but just at the point when sleep is about to overcome you - at least that was my experience. With all the usual defences relaxed in the hypnogogic phase of sleep all manner of fearful ideas and images creep up unexpectedly from the deepest recesses of the mind into consciousness. This is what would happen:

I would wake violently from the terror with my heart pumping so painfully fast it felt like my chest would rupture. On some occasions I would literally leap from my bed to find myself standing at the bedroom door gasping. The night terror was always about the *fear of death* - unadulterated by the usual defences - just that stark pure realisation that it would be happening to me sooner or later. No escaping.

I'd then rush breathless to my mother's side of their bed in sheer blind panic and try to snuggle up with her in my demented anxiety ridden state. It never occurred to me to rush to my father's side. I instinctively recognised I couldn't bank on any reassurance coming my way from him in the existential crisis department. He was dealing with his own version of it. My mother was the safer bet. Though it felt wrong and 'bad' to infiltrate the parental bed, these were exceptional circumstances. Normally I would get kicked out or be turfed onto the bedroom floor before morning when my mother would do her best to respond to my impossible existential questions:

"Mummy why do we have to die?"

(Uncomfortable silence as my poor mother tries to come up with an answer.)

"Mummy what happens when you die?"

'Umm..... no one really knows'

"But Mummy what will actually happen to *me* I mean?"

'Mmmm I don't know - well your body won't be here anymore.'

"But where will my body be?"

'Umm... well it will go back to the earth...... go back to nature.....'

"Oh that's horrible with all the worms and things. But what will happen to **me**?"

'Well I don't really know but maybe, umm, maybe when you die you go into a kind of pool.............. a pool of spirits.......'

"A pool of spirits, what like a lake?" I am trying to imagine the 'pool' and something doesn't wash.

'Ummmm, well yes, maybe the spirits all pool together......'

I knew she didn't believe a word of it, and I knew she knew I knew. Her explanation was entirely unsatisfactory to me. It was rubbish, sorry Mum. And more than that, a feeling of meaninglessness started to infiltrate and work its way into my small life. At first it sneaked up almost unnoticed and then it started to take hold. Everything was utterly pointless. I mean, seriously why bother if it all just ends like that? It all comes to nothing. Or a stupid 'pool'? I was inconsolable.

I found it incredible that people, everyone, just wandered the earth seemingly unaware and unbothered by this unacceptable state of affairs. Were they mad or deluded? How do you block out this unpalatable truth? Why wasn't everyone a jittering wreck like me? I know! Plan A: Lets find something so exciting and all consuming that it fills up the space presently occupied by the **gigantic fear monster.** And not just fills up the space, but zaps it with so much vitality and explosive activity that the fear finally gets wiped out. Failing that, it gives up and slinks away to some distant outpost in the far reaches of one's consciousness. It didn't work of course, so secretly I began to work on Plan B: What I could do to make damn sure I would live forever.

Later when I was heading for adolescence I made a vow to myself to fall in love so hard, so fast and so completely that **love itself would annihilate the fear** (I was way ahead of the times) and clearly going for a love oriented variant of Plan A. So when it came to my unwitting future partners they had their work cut out dealing with the deep life v. death intensity of my passion. How would they know not to take it personally?

Meanwhile my father seemed to be working up his own theories and hypotheses regarding this problematic, sleep deprived daughter of his. Surely it was something developmental, or oedipal or some kind of unconscious process manifesting as this obsession with death and dying etc etc? .... just something else, anything else, but it simply could not be what it seemed to be about. ***Nothing is ever what it seems to be about.*** Hold that thought because this concept is critical to the childrearing philosophy in our household.

- - - - - - - - - - - - - - -

```
Hi Dr M
I'm seriously into this writing business now.
Ain't no stopping me now - it's taken me over and
you didn't respond to my last email so hope you
don't mind me sending you this?
Kit
```

The Work Ethic

My father had his private practice at home which, as I have described, we moved and operated around. He was hugely dedicated to his patients and his practice, and to the philosophy. I try to imagine what it must have been like to be at the cutting edge in the applied/hands-on sense during the 1950's and 60's as an active and thoroughly engaged member of the evolving contemporary Freudian movement. That he thrived on challenging the status quo was a significant characteristic of his personality, and that this trait, or quality, could be creatively channeled into an exploration of the psyche and 'helping' people made absolute sense. When he was on form he had an insatiable curiosity and need to get below the surface of things ie people and situations and was pretty fearless in the exploration that that demanded. I admired him enormously (even in my more rebellious phases recognising that he too was a rebel) and sometimes envied his patients who unreservedly had his full and undivided attention (if only in 50 minute chunks). There were occasional references, albeit, mostly 'asides' that revealed that he felt psychoanalysis couldn't get to the heart of his own problems and wounds. It worked for everyone else but somehow never for him.

My father was trained by Anna Freud in Hampstead and starting sometime during the 1960s worked in the public sector setting up services too: In child guidance in North London, with adults in West London and at an adolescent drop in centre in Brent(for free as far as I am aware) with colleagues who were developing these services. He spent a considerable amount of time going to clinics and meetings in the evenings after he had finished his private practice. I never heard him complain about work or being overworked or say anything remotely negative relating to his working life. His only criticism of colleagues in the professional sense seemed to be reserved for the Kleinians and their theoretical position, and for the world of psychiatry in its refusal to recognise the value of the 'talking cure'. Despite my father's non conforming personality, he was dedicated to psychoanalytical principles and did not deviate from this course.

My mother went back to work when I was 12 as a senior registrar at Great Ormond Street Children's Hospital in London. When she didn't work she played Solitaire late into the night, and sometimes almost all night long, and it never looked as if anything other than the family and medicine (and Solitaire) could hold her interest. My father supported her fully to go back to work as soon as she felt she could. If my mother had been around for the advent of computer games I'm sure she would have been completely hooked.

She later became a consultant with her own EEG department. She was highly political and a staunch advocate of the NHS.

Sometimes she would be asked to give talks or lectures (the study of migraine was one of her hot subjects) and this she loathed, having a very shy temperament. Ironically, she would give the talk and then put herself to bed for days afterwards in a cool, darkened room nursing the intolerable migraine that invariably accompanied the release of tension. I guess she knew everything there was to know about migraines except how to stop them in the first place.

Occasionally, and usually only when asked, she would talk about her work and I remember her describing to us, babies whose brain waves revealed serious neural damage. One day it slipped out that she had been required to perform an EEG on Myra Hindley's brain in Holloway Prison. Mainly she spoke much less about her work than my father. She was reserved and extremely modest, personally and professionally. My father was Marion's great admirer and advocate.

My parents had met in Cape Town at the age of 17 at medical school before they came to London and married in 1950. I saw in the wedding photographs my dignified, upright mother - she was only 5'2" and a bit but always appeared taller - with her dark swept back hair and palest blue eyes, her scorpionic aqualine nose and high cheek bones. Her pale eyes became more piercing with the passing of time and her sculpted bone structure and tall forehead more pronounced. She had no idea how formidable she could seem - no sense whatsoever of the power of her presence. Next to her in those wedding photos, kind of laid back, was my bespectacled, smiling father in the days when he was slimmer and less shambolic looking, almost Woody Allenesque facially but fuller and more substantial in stature. As I think about their professional identities I begin to understand better the pressure for us to achieve. It must have been frustrating beyond belief for them to have encountered in me such a degree of indifference when it came to the realm of academia. It was a bit different with my brothers, as Sam found his niche academically early on (despite being regularly off his head on acid from his mid teens). Jake too, found a way through into his own creative identity (after accumulating a number of adolescent milestones such as getting arrested and detained for defacing a church door when stoned). I got there in the end via a circuitous (and at times precarious) route and was certainly a very late bloomer.

9: Spanish Guitar & other things.....

At 9 I was given my first classical guitar and lessons at the Spanish Guitar Centre in town. I was very eager to learn and master the guitar. Yes, it was a beautiful sounding instrument but more important, it was pretty cool to play guitar.

Getting to those lessons was also indirectly connected to first time I had an 'inappropriate sexual encounter' as they say. I would catch the tube from Finchley Road to Leicester Square on a busy Saturday morning for my guitar lessons. Stuck in a crowded carriage holding onto my clunky guitar case with one hand, clutching the handrail with the other, and pushed up against the bodies around me, I was vulnerable prey to any wandering hands. When it happened I was strangely calm and unafraid and more bemused than anything else. As this stranger's hand moved in on me the specific thought that went through my head was: *"This is strange. He's a grown up - he must know what he's doing."*

I knew not to hang around to expand on the thesis and jumped off at the next stop.

When I got home I told my mother that this man had done funny things with me. My parents found me a new guitar teacher within walking distance - just up the road.

9: A kid goes to a shrink

(but I still don't get the joke)

The First Cut is the Deepest...

9 is going to continue be an impressively eventful year, I discover, and it's going to be all about coming unstitched and then getting stitched up. There will be quite a few untidy threads sticking messily out everywhere, and no one is going to know what to do with them. Stuff that is way too convoluted for any kid to unravel or unpick is going to be offered up in a beautiful, entirely inappropriate intervention. And it's going to make a lasting impact, just sit back and watch:

- - - - - - - - - - - - - -

```
Hi Dr Maelstrum
I really wonder what you're going to make of this
next piece - if you can enlighten that would be
great.  I'd like your take on it.
Kit
```

- - - - - - - - - - - - - -

Sam kept razor blades. Admittedly, there was something rather glamorous and daring about them. He'd do clever, crafty things shaping up bits of wood, chopping insects in half (as boys do), secretly carving his initials into the legs of the kitchen table. So logically it followed that they, razor blades, would make great pencil sharpeners. I took one of them and put it in the pocket of my satchel. This particular day at school I had been fishing around in my satchel pocket looking for something when my finger met the razor blade. There was a lot of blood. To a freshly analysed and trained up Freudian this glorious (and rather gory) scenario was utterly irresistible: The Unconscious Motives for the Razor Blade Being in the Satchel in the first place? It was simply out of the question that it might have been there to...... sharpen pencils? Not a chance in hell. My father is in his element. I am in the first aid room.

The Razor Blade Incident lead me to the consulting room of Fat Ankles, my very first shrink. Although at the time I didn't know why I was there - strangely no one took it upon themselves to tell me - on reflection I was aware of the conspiratorial whispering of my parents and insistent checking up on my 'progress' that had seemed just plain weird and out of character with their normal benign neglect. Despite my relative youth even I could tell something serious was up and chances were, as usual, I had something to do with it.

I call her Fat Ankles not to be rude or disrespectful but because they, the ankles, were the most prominent part of her anatomy and the focus of my mainly downturned gaze for the duration of our 'work' together. As you can gather, I kept my head down.

Fat Ankles and I had a strange relationship. If ever I revealed anything that worried me - usually of a bodily nature - she seemed visibly disgusted. Her subtle facial expressions unmasked her genuine feelings, the impression being she had caught the whiff of something really nasty on my breath in the form of my unacceptable words. I felt humiliated and ashamed. I felt I contaminated the sanctity of her consulting room. I thought I was supposed to tell her these things? She is supposed to be ok with them, isn't she? You talk here about things you would never talk about at home (according to my father) and that's what is meant to happen, isn't it? I thought I was playing by the rules.

There were some safe subjects, so I thought: we talked horses - I loved horses just like I would grow to love boys with a raw romanticism and toe curling longing. I rode horses twice a week at Frith Manor Equestrian Centre and I naturally want to have my own horse (like I will one day want to have my own boyfriend) but as my parents endlessly remind me, we live in town, I will grow out of it and **what about my schoolwork?** Regardless, I am focussing my fantasy life on becoming a brilliant show jumper. With hindsight of course, the horse! Not so safe really. But whatever I brought, she responded with staggeringly out of context 'truths' at wildly inappropriate moments:

One day apropo of nothing she said *'Do you know you could cut yourself and the cut would be so very fine you wouldn't notice it and then you could bleed and bleed until you fainted?'*

At this point I was seeing Fat Ankles 3 times a week before school and the game plan had now radically changed: how to co-exist with the strange lady and her bizarre interjections? I couldn't escape her gaze. I was here not by choice and my keeper was worryingly odd, so I felt. Even a 9 year old can pick up that something is amiss upstairs. I was here, I recognised, to pacify my parents. I kept going and they kept feeling better. So meanwhile the space had to be filled with something - anything - and I worked damn hard to make sure it was.

Over time I learned how to say something apparently significant whilst being fully aware it meant nothing at all. I learned how to be present yet be utterly absent - I learned well how to keep Fat Ankles out of my psyche even though I couldn't keep her out of my sight. We settled into a rhythm, a guarded tactical exchange that lead us up a series of dead ends and inconsequential trails. I dreaded her and I envisioned her dread of me and my approaching 7 am footsteps to her door. She watched me as I watched her watching me. I played families with the bendy wire figures in the dolls house in the corner of her consulting room, keeping a sharp eye on her movements from behind the curtains of my unruly hair. I had stopped listening but I learned from then to check my body for any fine cuts that might lead to my fainting through loss of blood. I checked often and I kept on checking. And then I checked some more. I didn't trust my body. I didn't feel safe in a body. I didn't feel safe anywhere. My body would, I knew, ultimately betray me as all bodies must, but not just yet please - I was only 9 and acquiring life skills fast.

Ezra throughout these years, as I said, developed the annoying habit of linking the 'help' I was supposedly getting to any small successes I legitimately earned through my own creativity and dedication: the music I played and made up, the sporting achievements, the 'doing well at school' and being a popular kid. I could have hit him and almost did. *Then* I understood why people self harm. I could barely repress my rage.

There was a simple awkward truth that seemed to have eluded the relevant adults. Being sent outside the family to talk about the family itself - its secrets (though I had no clue yet what they were), its lies, its impossible expectations - would always feel like an act of betrayal. Was I supposed to betray the very people on whom I was wholly dependent?

When I reached eleven I was let out for good behaviour. I had served 2 years.

- - - - - - - - - - - - - -

PS Dr M:
If you're anything like Fat Ankles please say something now and we can cancel my provisional appointment. I hope you get where I'm coming from? No disrespect to the profession.
Kit

Eleven +

I Want to Hold Your Hand...

I'm now 11 heading for 12. I feel incredibly grown up anyway. I wear make up to cover the spreading forest of adolescent spots on my forehead. I wear make up to look as old as I can. If the wearing of make up were a way to speed up the growth process I would wear even more. I would slap on the pan stick like my life depended upon it. I am planning my great escape from the grammar school I now go to, the one my parents have always wanted for me. Suddenly I've stopped playing sport, I've stopped making art, I've stopped learning in the conventional sense. I've even almost stopped riding horses. Very soon I'll be getting 27% in chemistry. I think that will be an all time record low and I will be proud of it, sort of, when I can hold back the shame.

My mother takes me to see the Beatles at the Finsbury Park Astoria. I feel really sorry for my quiet reserved mother and confused by my feelings because it's so lovely she's taken me. The Fab 4 are lowered onto the stage in a plywood 'helicopter'. The screaming is overwhelming. My mother hangs on in there flanked at all sides by hysterical, sweating, adolescent screamers and me. The smell of BO, Brut and 4711 cologne is emanating from the pores of the swooning masses all around us. I think of her, my mother, as someone who rarely allows herself any pleasure. I wish she would. This is not pleasurable. She doesn't know how much I want to love her, because right now I am my father's daughter bonded more to him than her. It's just how it is, known and awkwardly accepted in the family. I feel guilty as hell. The screaming intensifies in waves - I have no sense of what song they are now playing. It could be 'Love Me Do' but then it could be a dozen others. I can't hear a thing. I don't know whether to participate with the throbbing mass or hide under my seat. I look at Mum - an island of dignified stillness in the midst of all the madness or is it that she's traumatised? She doesn't know how much I admire her because she puts up with all of us, and this. I am frightened of the look in her eyes. I see a sorrow that goes way back to some godforsaken muddy backwater in Lithuania where she was born - what she escaped from, pogrommed out aged 2 with the other bedraggled peasant families. I see that same look in my own eyes when caught off guard, an ancestral ghost of a look in the hall mirror, a haunting that is in me too. I look just like her but blondish.

We shuffle our way out of the velvet festooned Astoria amidst the throng of adolescent hysterics and their white-faced parents and go gratefully home, a little bit closer, after a hell of a seriously hard days night.

My mother is incredibly intelligent and there is a myth in the family that her own mother, Rose, was an early proto feminist. My father points out however that his mother-in-law 'was a cold and distant parent' a statement applied to most of the parents of most of the people he knows. We have all heard it countless times. Do any parents exist, one may wonder, who are not cold and distant?

Another myth or possible truth propagated in the family is that the clever educated Jews in Lithuania escaped to the USA whilst the unskilled peasants ended up in South Africa, as a result of the pogroms. Her's and my father's families washed up in South Africa and I thereby deduct we are basically of ignorant peasant stock. My mother has acquired her acute pragmatic intelligence somewhere along the line, because of or in spite of this.

My father tells me my mother and Sam are the 'geniuses of the family' whilst he and I are the ones with the 'artistic temperament'. I do like the sound of this though I discover much later what he's really talking about. For now I am gloriously in the dark. I take a look at the score sheet: Jake sits somewhere in the middle as far as his IQ is concerned. He's seen the numbers too and it matters. In fact he keeps seeing the numbers because we are all tested numerous times and in various new-fangled ways perhaps in the hope that our IQ's will collectively go up.

My mother has values I admire, professionally, politically, socially and yet I've never come across anyone whose sense of self is so utterly diminished. It scares me. I want to make it better.

I can't. I start thinking of her as 'Marion' rather than 'Mum' to see if that feels any better. It doesn't. She holds us all together, especially my father, who I will grow to recognise falls dramatically apart and often. Around the time I go to see Fat Ankles there is clearly more than one elephant in the room yet to be outed. By the time I leave Fat Ankles the elephant is still very much there.

My Father

(I have only one father, but it doesn't always feel like it)

It's like this between the patient & the shrink:
One will free associate while the other tries to tell you
What they think that you might think
Plenty of them around & strangely, mainly in north London
Mecca of the swallowed back persona, deeply deep in diagnosis
A penny for your thoughts, a pound for your psychosis

Sam and I have a game called Count the Shrinks. It's summer and wandering around our leafy block we have now counted 13 shrink residences and their numbers are growing. My brother is making up 5 bar gates. These are just the ones we know about. As we live in NW3 - it's not so surprising, we are in the Mecca of the shrink kingdom. Anna Freud is over there in Maresfield Gardens and the Tavistock (alien out of bounds Kleinian territory) is down the road in Belsize Park. Sam knows the score. He has been 'seeing somebody' for longer than I have. My younger brother Jake has yet to start.

My father is always playing it down. Look at those anal Kleinians! They make their kids go Five Times a Week! I had been going 3 times, my brother 4 so we are creeping perilously close to the number that represents something wholly unacceptable. The rivalry (or perhaps 'war' is a better description) between the Freudians and the Kleinians is raked over heatedly at their bridge parties, dinner parties - other peoples' bridge and dinner parties, soundbites overheard later at home by us messing around on the stairs casually eves dropping in on their conversations. I have no idea what it's about but I now associate the list of 'bad' things and the crucifix finger gesture commonly used to ward off evil, with the less than holy ethics and practices of the Kleinians. No one I know is called Melanie.

Ezra is a maverick and an iconoclast: a funny, warm, liberal-thinking, ex communist party member (South Africa pre 1950) type of shrink. He is the best broad-minded, free-thinking Dad you could hope for, most of the time. I adore him, naturally, and he and I are creative kindred spirits when it comes to art, music, film (not books, please note) and the wearing of ash encrusted jeans which he does even when he is seeing his patients. There's something instinctively compassionate and soulful about Dad and you can feel it. Our house is a sanctuary for less blessed kids to hang out and escape their own draconian parents. You can get lost in this house. We have kids, cats, lodgers, friends, friends of friends, patients, au pairs, fish, a couple of tortoises, parents of course, gerbils. Later the list will include boyfriends, girlfriends and their friends and relations and many more generations of cats with unusual names, courtesy of my father's vivid imagination, such as Saratoga, Baby Coco and Faluloo.

The human component of the above list (and the opportunistic feline too) will amass round the kitchen table pretty much 24 hours a day: Breakfast, snacks, brunch, lunch, afternoon tea, dinner, late supper, midnight feasts and middle of the night insomniac biscuit eating, all washed down with gigantic pots of tea and infused with the aroma of cigarette smoke in the intervals between other excuses for eating and meeting. At all times activity of some sort or another will constellate around the bashed up badly formica'ed kitchen table which is the mecca of our family life.

My father is the life and soul, the jazz playing cool dude. There's plenty of Miles, Roland and Theolonius, Ella, Bill Evans and his favourite, Anita O'Day. There is Jazz on a Summer's Day. My father is open-minded with his tastes and will soon discover James Taylor and Joni Mitchell before his kids do. How cool is that? He is a pioneer of tolerance and benign human exploration. You can tell him anything - nothing can shock him - and he listens and responds openly, wholeheartedly, empathically. He can make you feel as if you matter because you do. You do matter, for now. You can talk to him about sex without feeling ashamed. What Ezra likes and doesn't like will not always follow a pattern. He really doesn't like RD Laing.

And then there's this other person periodically living in the house with us, who will be found in bed largactilled*, mogodonned**, mandraxed***, valiumed****, and eventually I discover but not quite yet, vodka'd *****unconscious. Before he is entirely swallowed up by an oblivion only partly of his own making he will have raged and snarled at anything and anyone in his path. Jake is the one who gets it in the neck for simply being the youngest whilst my father's jealousy is disinhibited by the combination of substances co mingling in his bloodstream. By now he will have enveloped the house in ear splitting full volume Wagner or Beethoven (no more jazz), stumbled into items of furniture and strangely, asked me in detail about my schoolwork. I know he has no real interest in my schoolwork or in me right now. I learn quickly to see this as a marker, a sign of his probable descent, as if to show an interest might keep him with us in this consensual world just a little longer.

Cool Dad has been replaced by Tyrannical Wagnerian Dad; Tyrannical Dad will succumb to full, stony cold unconsciousness any minute now. It happens so fast I barely notice en route the man/baby that is now my father, but I hear his muffled dislocated pre-verbal cries from behind the bedroom door. His regression is almost complete. Only one step away now from permanent and timeless oblivion, the step my mother will keep him from making as she has faithfully done for longer than I have been alive. This is the deal.

The household will then go into a kind of hushed mourning. The friends, boyfriends, girlfriends and extraneous relatives will be long gone. The remaining inhabitants will tread eggshells and potential visitors will be warned off long before they get anywhere near the house. The outer world will need to keep its distance and the world inside these walls its silence, until the slow and painful process of each period of recovery has taken its course.

But I am cheating a bit here and getting way ahead of myself because I don't discover the full graphic, anatomical detail until I am around 16 or 17. All I know is that something is askew in this kingdom. I love these people, my parents, in a way that sometimes physically hurts, though I am desperate to get away from them and I sometimes want to put my hand in that electric fire.

Footnotes:

- *Largactil - for severe depression, behavioural disorders & nausea. Addictive in long term use.
- **Mogadon - for severe insomnia. Drowsiness may last into the next day.
- ***Mandrax - for insomnia & anxiety - life threatening if mixed with alcohol. Now banned.
- ****Valium - for treatment of anxiety disorders, muscle spasms etc. Dependency likely in longterm use.
- *******Vodka - for immediate short term relief of all of the above symptoms with the exception of nausea.**

More About The Deal

Have You Seen Your Mother, Baby, Standing in the Shadow?

There is a beautiful and simple symmetry that is the deal my parents have struck with each other:

When he's good he's very, very good. And when he's bad, he is so damn bad it defies description.

Marion on the other hand is consistently low level depressed. Not non functioning depressed but just plain simple Sad. There's no getting away from it. I see it in her, I dread the idea of being like her, not because I don't admire her many qualities but because she is so deeply unhappy and it shows. She has no self appreciation and believes she has little to offer even though she is highly educated and respected and will soon be a successful consultant with her own department in the NHS. She makes elaborate, time-consuming Robert Carrier dishes for dinner parties not out of enjoyment but because she has to compensate for her supposed low key presence, or so she believes. I'm not making it up, she told me this. My mother is often seen with a cigarette in one hand and a dishcloth in the other.

When my father is good ie not on a bender, he engages with life with a massive irrepressible appetite. Sometimes this will go on for years without relapse. He is sensate pleasure personified and his warmth draws people out of themselves as they gravitate towards him. His appreciation knows few limitations. And he takes my reticent mother with him. He brings her to life, or brings life all the way to her, which ever way you want to look at it. He forces an engagement with the outer world and breathes fire into her depleted world. He stokes up her fading greying embers into a bright, oxygenated furnace. Everything is in multiples: There are trips and concerts, there are museums and contemporary art galleries, films and plays, people to connect with and new places to go, there are politics to wind people up with. He is always just about to overstep the mark. He talks 'personal' to strangers. He undresses unashamedly on beaches in full frontal view. He is the one who body surfs the tsunamic sea even though the red flag is up waving furiously and search & rescue are in the skies above him. I'm not being metaphorical either. He grabs life by the horns......

When my father is bad (and you know how bad, bad is) my mother brings him back from the brink. His depression is radical too. She then becomes the one who saves his life or if you like, makes sure he at least, stays alive. She nurses him back piece by piece into life and patiently sits out his detoxification. At home, in hospital, both. The world he has brought to life for her she now keeps at bay. Patients who he has forgotten to cancel on the outbound descent get tactfully, delicately, ushered away at the door when they turn up for their usual appointment. Colleagues' calls are intercepted, then deflected. It's her turn. A kind of unspoken payback for his gift of life to her sad under valued self.

I am becoming complicit too in the personal and professional protection of my father because outside of this state, what he brings to the world is so hugely and undeniably deserving of that protection. So subtle, though, is my enlistment over time into the role of my mother's assistant, I barely register it.

- - - - - - - - - - - - - -

```
Hi Dr M
Hope you're getting the gist now? Sorry it's
taking so long to write this thing. Your silence
is a bit disturbing.
Kit
```

Enter the Gypsy

Into The Mystic...

Sometime around my 12th year my mother takes me to see a newly released feature film called *'Sky West & Crooked'* which is on at the local ABC cinema in Hampstead.

Starring is a baby-faced Hayley Mills (British child actress known primarily for her roles in Disney movies), the director is her father John Mills and her mother, Mary Hayley Bell, has co written the screenplay. I don't think my own mother has quite cottoned on to the central themes of the story until it is too late and I am slumped back in my velveteen seat, tucking into my Walls vanilla and chocolate ice cream tub and she is lighting up one of her John Players.

Hayley Mills normally plays the banal and fluffy characters that you'd expect to encounter in good wholesome family-entertainment-type movies. Not this time. This time round she is Brydie - a highly traumatised, dissociated and possibly retarded 17 year old, who as a much younger kid has been implicated in an accident where a childhood friend, whilst playing around with his father's shotgun, has died. She remembers absolutely nothing about it and this incident has arrested her development in all ways imaginable. She now spends her time entirely avoiding growing up and instead hangs around graveyards nurturing a fascination for the dead animals which she will bury and then exhume. And to complicate everything further, she has a dying alcoholic mother.

The villagers fear for their own kids (she is a kind of overgrown ringleader) and fear too for her as she is fast becoming a sexualised adult threatening to lead the whole lot of them astray whilst remaining entirely oblivious to her own power and influence over the younger kids. Oh dear, what to do with Brydie? Where to put her? How to control her? How to curtail the florid passions that any day soon will be arising in her?

Enter the gypsies, especially one of them who happens to be played by an electrifyingly dark and handsome newcomer called Ian McShane. He pulls a suicidal Brydie out of the treacherous river and saves her from herself. Not only that, he seems to be attracted to her, to want to be close to her, despite all her obvious flaws, mental abberations and general strangeness of character. It bothers him not one iota. You can see the resolution a mile away - but dare the writers pull it off? Well, that's the cliff hanger that has now made me drop my plastic spoon and lose all interest in my ice cream.

On the scrubby windy moor, the enigmatic Gypsy and a tousled Brydie fashion a ring of their entwined hair strands, intermingled, hers naturally a white blond and his of course, black (true to the stereotype) and I suddenly get it. And not just in a cognitive sense, but my gut and various body parts are responding in complete agreement: We all need a Gypsy Lover (or Ian McShane) to save us from our dreary and stultifying lives of convention and constriction. Someone who couldn't care less about the flaws, mental illnesses, traumas or bizarre idiosyncrasies that have everyone else running for cover. Someone who will love us irrespective of our past, present and future fuck ups. Someone who isn't obligated to play by the rules. In return the deal is a life on the road, and most probably one of poverty, exclusion and marginalization but seriously, it's a complete no brainer. Especially when the Gypsy Lover is the breathtakingly lovely Ian McShane. Somehow or another (and I can't quite remember how) Brydie does eventually get to go off into a new life with her gypsy at the very end, although it's touch and go for a while, before the audience is mercifully relieved of the tension.

There is no way my mother could have guessed the impact these film scenes would make as they ignite this slumbering archetype, for eons embedded in an ancient and forgotten place in my own psyche. That the animus in me has arrived out of the mystic fully formed as the Gypsy Lover is the awkward, irreversible revelation, and the genesis of an enduring longing for a particular kind of heartfelt union. All my parents' best laid plans for my happy and trouble-free future have been entirely compromised and decimated from this day forth. And we are all (especially me) currently oblivious to this fact.

World view according to the 13 year old

If You're Going to San Francisco...

It's difficult to remember the exact order of things because the year I turn 13 so much happens - is it the traumatisation that has addled my brain - flooded my amygdala? Jumbled things up? Or is it the electrocution?

It's 1967. I've been through the Mary Quant inspired Vidal Sassoon asymmetrical haircut phase and as it grows out my excessively curly wild hair will not be straightened into submission the way I'd like it to be. I've tried everything: sellotape, hair straighteners, chemical treatments and now finally, the iron. I am alone in the TV room where we do the ironing, my head is on the ironing board and I am just starting to get down to business when there's a small explosion in my hand. The bakelite handle of the (ancient) iron has welded itself to my palm while sparks are spitting out of the plug socket. And just like in the movies the volts paralyse my hand so I can't drop the bloody thing. If you've never been electrocuted you will not understand the particular way in which the brain can no longer tell the body what to do. I had accidentally stuck my fingers inside a light socket once before so the experience wasn't entirely unfamiliar. But on this occasion the violent shaking has taken a hold and doing my best to scream, I somehow throw the treacherous iron to the floor. My mother comes rushing up the stairs (plus cigarette and dishcloth). I am literally white with shock and have a burn mark on my hand where the bakelite handle got fused to my skin. My hair is more frizzy than ever.

I'm spared any more ironing catastrophes that year when the Summer of Love comes crashing and jingling into the parks and streets of the city bringing with it a Whole New Look. At last! It's great to have the hair I've been trying to get rid of all these years. There is something about me that doesn't need to be changed. Yes, now it's really trendy to be frizzy and have enormous out of control hair. What a gift. I now avoid ironing. But then, apart from the hair, I soon acquire a wardrobe that will never need ironing anyway.

This year we will have the most enormous and infamous house party (while the folks are away) and the place will get trashed. I will be introduced to the beat poets; I will get arrested for 'loitering with intent'; I will meet a man who writes to me from prison; I will start smoking weed with my friend Candace and I will discover I can put cigarettes out with my bare feet. Also I will get molested by an old man at sea. Oh, I almost forgot, midway through the year I'll be back in analysis with a new shrink.

Smoking with Candace

"Love is like a cigarette,

the bigger the drag, the more you get" - *Adrian Mitchell*

Candace is someone I meet loosely through the heroin addicted daughter of a family friend. Candace is the most unusual person I've ever encountered. She is 15 and therefore two whole years older than me. She has a job in a hairdressers down on Finchley Road. I don't think she's been to school for quite a while. This idea is very attractive to me, since I am 'officially still at school' though my teachers might take issue with this statement.

Candace lives just up the same road as us at the top of the hill in a dilapidated, slightly creepy, early Edwardian house with her mother, a 'former starlet' in Candace's words, much in the vein of Bette Davis in Whatever Happened to Baby Jane. They have about 10 or so Golden Labradors. There is newspaper all over the floor for the dogs and apart from them, and since this house is huge and contains only Candace and her mother, it feels empty and neglected (much like Candace, no doubt.)

At first it seems that Candace is living there alone. I'm impressed. She is enviably self sufficient. On rare occasions I notice the presence of someone else shuffling round the house who drinks heavily before lunchtime and talks animatedly presumably to 'someone': I am introduced to Candace's starlet mother who has blond 1940's permed hair and the bright voluptuous lips you associate with the early days of Hollywood. Candace on the other hand is small and dark with long straight hair (the sort I'd always coveted pre 1967) and it's hard to imagine how they can possibly be related. Candace introduces me to smoking weed.

Since I already smoke cigarettes (No 6 is the smoke of my choice) it's only a small step away. My parents who are both doctors and chain smokers, like the majority of their contemporaries, have realised that two out of their three kids - by 13 and 14 - are already addicted. Not surprising since we were both conceived and gestated by parents with high levels of nicotine in their bloodstreams, brought choking into a world contaminated by their billowing smoke and reared amongst the ashtrays and butt ends that squat in every room of the house. In my father's consulting room is the King of Ashtrays - a parting gift from a patient. It's bright mustard yellow, about the size of a frisbee and full to the brim.

My parents have a rather unenlightened attitude to our smoking habits. We are allowed to smoke at weekends only! Imagine if they were only allowed to smoke at weekends? They have collectively repressed all knowledge of the unremitting nature of addiction when it comes to their own children. Their dictate however, drives me up the road to Candace's house where her mother is well beyond caring how much of what is smoked when.

Candace intrigues me. She appears to have come into the world entirely without parents in the normal sense of the word. I can't imagine that she has a father - though biology determines that somewhere on this earth he has once existed and may still roam. Theoretically the person she lives with is her mother, though the theory isn't worth the paper it's written on when translated into practice. No evidence whatsoever. Candace therefore, is the first virtually parent-free kid I've met. I'm not sure what I feel about it.

Sometimes we hang out in our favourite coffee bar in Heath Street which is called the Exotic. It's opposite the boutique where only a year ago I was buying my Mary Quant yellow and purple giant daisy dresses and Courreges' white cut-out boots. Now the uniform is tattered jeans with cigarette ash rubbed into them (to encourage the stressed look) loose fitting holey jumpers and on the occasions when shoes really have to be worn (such as when it's snowing), then desert boots are the thing. I acquire a leather dustman's jerkin that I am very proud of. The walking ashtray look is pretty cool.

I drop round to Candace's place on my way home from school in the early spring afternoons. She rolls a joint or maybe two, and we stare out of the window at the overgrown, brambled and tangled up jungle that is Candace's garden, making up stories of our eventual escape. The house is quiet, Bette Davis has taken herself off to bed. The dogs are settled. In the gap between absconding from school and going home for dinner everything is ok in this small stoned world:

Peace. Peace at last.

I now write songs so sometimes I bring my guitar up the hill to her place and Candace is audience to my latest adolescent lament. She is re assuringly melancholic and attuned to the gist of the oeuvre - I silently appreciate her for being free of judgement and so on the wave length.

And I hope too, in the stillness of these moments, that my friend and almost orphan, Candace, will be alright.

The Party

The Eve of Destruction

The party was destined to happen - it was written in some Great Book somewhere that it would come to pass. Just like a wet London August, nothing could stop it arriving. All the necessary ingredients had come together: naïve enthusiasm, the perfect venue and an absence of responsible elders - the vital elements to ensure its manifestation, no matter what.

Our parents were abroad for a few weeks and it wasn't unusual for us to be left in the care of other people, usually and in this case, whatever au pair we had at the time. And usually and certainly in this case, they would be almost as young as we were and probably quite bored too.

All that summer we'd been hanging out at various gatherings on Saturday nights or on rainy Sunday afternoons in and around Hampstead. It would all be word of mouth.

"So and so is having a gathering!"

'Whatsit's parents are out of town!'

"It's happening at so and so's place"

'D'you think we can score some weed there?'.

The kids in our circle were upping the pressure for us to take advantage of our parent-free zone.

Getting a gathering going: It would invariably start small with a few key players looking to get in on the action - just somewhere to go to relieve the stultifying boredom of the extra long summer holidays. Next a few older kids would catch on and then their peers and consequently it would snowball out of control. And thus, the mass would be mobilised. A bit like a flash mob before the invention of the mobile. The speed at which word got around before the advent of the technology was impressive.

It mattered not whose beautiful home was about to be blindly and anarchically invaded, occupied and casually destroyed by the marauding hormonal mass before it moved psychopathically on and out to its next target. Really it was beyond mattering because it wasn't your property to worry about. "What is property? Property is theft." But it was going to matter to us a bit more than we had anticipated.

So knowing the way these things evolved it was obvious more people would show up than had been invited, though just how many more was the unanswerable question. The true potential of this freshly liberated space - our house - had been wasted on the dreary parties and events the parents had throw over the years. It begged, pleaded, to be given something genuinely worthwhile to celebrate. The parquet floor downstairs that had been embossed with the imprint of hundreds of stilettoed heel marks from some earlier, less exciting era, was about to be anointed by a new barefoot generation. It wouldn't know what hit it.

Don't wanna dance? Come on in anyway, friend, just lose yourself upstairs then, plenty of places and spaces to get wasted and do whatever the hell you want. Come on in! Yes, definitely. And come on in they did, in droves.

I've consulted Sam about what happened next, because I simply do not remember very much at all. I've assumed that my not remembering is because I am off my head for most of the night, rather than just plain dissociated, but who knows? Here are some facts, thoughts, notes and musings in no particular order though pretty much as my jumbled up brain perceives them upon waking the next morning:

Sam tells me there were a couple of hundred very diverse people and they had a wild time. He tells me too they were all ages across the generations, upward from ours almost to our parents. Really? This I find extremely hard to believe though somewhere in my consciousness I remember some people with beards. He tells me everyone said this 'this party will go down in history'.

We notice a considerable amount of slimy yellow stuff is dripping from the walls which turns out to be smashed eggs and it does strike me this is a fairly interesting thing to do with an egg. But why? And where did so many eggs come from? And how do we get them off?

As he fills me in, the thought comes to me: *I am more in control of my life than others realise, seriously, this may be my trump card.* Though that I am thinking this particular thought at this particular moment may appear paradoxical in the extreme. I'll get back to this one later as it may be important.

We know that all the carefully selected cases of wine my father has stashed away have been discovered, recovered, exhumed and consumed. This is a bit worrying. We notice that every other drop of alcoholic substance in the house has been consumed too. Everything, even stuff in the cleaning cupboard seems to be missing. Lots of things are missing. There is broken furniture in the garden and it appears to have been thrown off the balcony. We need a plan. And glue.

I understand now what it means to 'live in the moment' because anticipating the future has become too terrifying a prospect to engage with. I will do that as much as I can.

I'm not quite sure what's happened to Jake or where he is, or who is supposed to be looking after him (he is only 7 or is he 8, I can't quite remember?). Ah, there he is, snoozing in the corner over there snuggled up with Saratoga (massive longhaired ginger tom). This is a relief.

I blearily bang into some people in the house who are making breakfast and it smells great. I don't know who they are and/or where they come from. I've never seen them before. Some have American accents and other accents that might be European. I discover soon they have every intention of staying here for a while, maybe for the next few days, or maybe a week? Supposing they never leave?

I know things have needed a good shaking up round here and I'm glad it's happened. I think I am happy, even though I should be wracked with guilt, anxiety and remorse as I survey the wreckage. For some inexplicable reason, I am not. Does this make me a 'bad' person? This is a very new experience. Voices of self harm? Seem to have vanished for now.

I feel sad. I think Candace has missed a great party. I wonder where on earth she is?

The Morning After

In the days after the party and sometime before the return of the parents I have a few strange and intriguing dreams which is not surprising as we are now living in a parallel universe. Our house has become a small commune inhabited by people we've only just met. They all seem to have somewhere else to live but right now they would prefer to live here with us, which, though I would never admit it to anyone, ever, I find flattering. This is the one dream that stuck and I wrote it down:

I dream that I am in the kitchen sitting with people I don't know very well, people a bit like the ones squatting with us right now, but not quite. We're talking about colour. This intense dark eyed, goatee bearded guy is giving an informal lecture: 'Do you know it's possible to see other colours?" 'What d'you mean, other colours?" I'm speaking like an idiot, my mouth is dry and rubbery. My tongue feels enormous. He goes on "Colours that you've never seen before, no one's ever seen them before because they're not on the Speckrum" "The Speckrum, what's the Speckrum?" I'm confused. He holds up a slim perspex block almost like a wand, with lines of colour on it. (I'm thinking, this must be the "Speckrum".) He holds it up so it catches the light coming through the kitchen window. "Colour that is there, been there all the time, but you can't see it. Except if you blink first like this (he blinks) and look now you can see it. See?" "No, can't see a thing" "Just let your eyes go lazy" "Lazy?" "Yes, really lazy" "Yup! I see it."

I wake up incredibly thirsty.

My Brother and the Beat Poets

"I saw the best minds of my generation destroyed by madness, starving hysterical naked, dragging themselves through the negro streets at dawn looking for an angry fix, angelheaded hipsters burning for the ancient heavenly connection to the starry dynamo in the machinery of night..."
- Howl by Allen Ginsberg

My brother Sam is pretty cool considering he's 14, therefore a year older but still somewhat smaller than me in stature. We have a complex relationship to do with size and bodies and intellect. He came into the world pre-mature and tiny, screamed for months and possibly even years, got very sick and nearly died and has consequently eaten a diet of mashed bananas and gorgonzola (plus the occasional egg) for much of his childhood. This is all he wants to eat and it may well be that his body knows exactly which specific nutrients found in bananas and Italian cheese it is deficient in.

When Sam was only 3 months old, I turned up in my mother's womb. I was subtitled the 'happy accident'. At the time the very last thing my mother wanted was to be pregnant again since every ounce of her energy was expended attempting to keep alive her tiny, unwell baby boy.

But I kept a low profile and floated silently and stealthily around in her unsuspecting uterus almost hoping she wouldn't notice too soon. Undeniably, my timing was atrocious and my mother's womb a hotbed of anxiety and foreboding. Later she would tell me that she feared giving birth to another premature ailing baby. I wasn't. I was the trouble-free smiley sort who ate, slept, laughed and thrived - for a while at least.

Sam, it turns out, is extremely clever (so his precarious start in life has not impeded his developing neural circuits). He has won a scholarship to a boys public school in Hertfordshire. Despite my healthier size and physical superiority Sam has been the victor in every game we've ever played. I've been trying to outwit him for as long as I can remember, to absolutely no effect. That I feel big, clumsy and stupid, is no surprise. We have been arch rivals since the year dot. Suddenly though, when I am 6 and Sam is 7 we are allies. How does this change occur within the pattern of our relationship? The arrival of the younger one, of course! Now we have a mutual interest in sticking together, whilst we watch our baby brother, Jake, lap up each precious drop of our mother's undivided attention. Everyone is sick with jealousy, including my father, as you know.

Anyway, my precocious older brother has already discovered the beat poets. He has "Wholly Communion" sitting in his bookshelf though whether he actually attended the 'Happening' itself at the Albert Hall is up for debate and unlikely. He is an avid reader of everything. I do not read at all. Too busy to read, don't understand the attraction. I'm very impressed when I hear our party hangers-on, these people who are currently living in our house, discussing poets that Sam has already consumed, digested and could probably recite from memory. We are talking serious stuff: Allen Ginsberg, Lawrence Ferlinghetti, Adrian Mitchell who if you listen, will 'tell me (& you) lies about Vietnam'. The names are poetic and exotic in themselves to my untutored ear in the same way that words like Kerouac or Cassidy roll off the tongue and have a certain alluring mystique. I've been told there are some interesting expletives within these poetic texts.

We're all going off to Speaker's Corner soon to recite their words and possibly try to get arrested. We'll see.

Rag Taggle Gypsy Fur Clad Bunch

We are a strange bunch: There is Len who towers over us, he's a "serious academic" though I never get to find out what he actually studies. He is quite a bit older - his hair may even be receding and he has John Lennon glasses. He's the one who makes the breakfast and generally looks after us - unofficial father figure minus any authority whatsoever over us. Not quite sure where he fits into the scheme of things, but he is close 'buddies' with Randy and Jeff. R & J are a couple of diplomats kids who go to the American School in St. Johns Wood. They are currently living in one of the red brick mansion blocks that we pass by on the bus near Lord's Cricket ground. Randy has bushy bright-carrot wild hair and wears an old First World War army jacket he's just picked up from Portobello Road. Jeff is more subdued - he doesn't have the carrot coloured hair - I'm intrigued and attracted by his assured introversion, perhaps because I'm probably an introvert myself in need of some encouraging role models. Randy & Jeff must be about 16 or 17. Jeff is the elder and the one most into the poetry. They have an extraordinarily handsome British friend called Chris in a Victorian policeman's cape who is camping out in our TV room with his German girlfriend, Carolla.

Before we set off, under her instruction Carolla and I have been rummaging through the contents of my mother's wardrobe - a looming monstrosity of a piece of furniture shipped all the way from Cape Town a few years earlier. She and I are searching for something floor-length and dramatic and if possible, a little strange and off beat. Carolla has decided I need sorting out and suggests I ditch the ash jeans for once and get a bit, you know, *experimental.* It's the middle of the summer but the wearing of fur to Speakers Corner seems right somehow. My mother's mink coat is too stuffy and puffy, too old fashioned and unflattering. One for the reject pile then. My grandmother's scrawny old rabbit skin jacket is more like it and it smells like it hasn't been worn for centuries. It's even better with the sleeves ripped off - like a sophisticated version of the leather dustman's jerkin. The only floor-length possibilites we can find are part of Marion's formal 'evening wear' ensemble, entombed in plastic dry cleaning bags that can't have seen the light of day for a while. The sort of thing she might wear if she ever accompanied Ezra to his Psychoanalytic Conventions, which as far as I can make out she rarely does and avoids like the plague. I haven't seen her wear this stuff in years so I doubt she'd mind us giving it an airing.

Then in the back recesses of the wardrobe we discover a battered tan leather suitcase full of 1940s and maybe 1950's silk and cotton skirts. The kind that are gathered and voluminous and covered in swirling abstracts, lines and spots and Kandinsky-like forms. There are more figurative designs too like the one I dig out with Eiffel towers etched into the weave and floating with the movement of the material along its folds. Then my fingers are all over a piece of fabric covered in tropical fruit and peacocks. Who thought these up and why? But it's the cotton slub skirt with the lime green and grey lemons that my eyes get fixated upon and I'm touching it and then sniffing it. Perhaps my brain chemistry has been altered by the colour dream or by other recent indulgences and experimentations: Something like a camera shutter clicks open in my mind; then as if carried by a wave of intense nostalgia I'm travelling with the lime-green-lemon skirt material across the oceans, beyond the equator to the southern hemisphere and to Cape Town. This is what I remember:

I'm very small, about 2 or 3, we're walking along a busy shopping street. Sam is there too, trying to keep up with Mum whose heals are clacking and slipping hurriedly along the cobbled pavement making a disproportionately loud sound. I'm holding onto her skirt with both hands and tripping pathetically along behind her, red-faced and wailing pitifully. I'm terrified, of what, I do not know. Losing Mum? Getting lost? Mum getting lost? The only thing that keeps the 'dreaded something' from happening is the lemon skirt fabric I'm currently grasping hold of because I feel the world, as I know it, will end if I let go.

We're on the upper deck of the No. 2 bus now trundling towards Hyde Park and our Speakers' Corner destination. I'm excited at the prospect though still pre occupied by the disturbing Cape Town memory and a little bit too warm in all this slightly smelly rabbit fur. Jake has willingly tagged along with us, I don't think I've seen him this happy, ever. The muscles at the corners of his mouth are struggling to reposition themselves in response to this

69

unusual feeling state. Perhaps it's all the extra attention he's been receiving from these unfamiliar people - gatecrashers in his evolving universe - and he's clearly thriving on it. Our au pair, who is supposed to be looking after him, hasn't been seen since the night of the party.

We are The Rag Taggle Gypsy Fur Clad Bunch.

We do not get arrested after all and I will learn something significant for my future development:

It is very difficult to get arrested when you're trying to but it is unbelievably easy when you are not.

I'm pretty sure Candace would agree.

The Return

Just before our temporary commune breaks up - due to the imminent return of the parents - we collectively attempt an exercise in damage limitation. Sam has a post office savings account which covers the replacement of most of the contents of the drinks cabinet. Some of the bottles we have to replace were already half drunk by the parents so in the name of authenticity we are obliged to drink a fair bit to get them back to those levels. Despite the fact that Sam has been saving up for years he doesn't seem to begrudge spending his precious dosh in this manner. Maybe he feels it was worth it? Perhaps being co-host of the 'best party ever' has softened the blow and given him something to be truly proud of? We've found a couple mops to sponge the egg off the walls and ceiling. The place seems to look ok superficially, but it has the air of having gone through something traumatic and the walls are looking somewhat blotchy from all the scrubbing, but only on close inspection. There's also a peculiar smell that none of us can quite identify. Perhaps a mixture of residual dope smoke, cat piss and the putrefying egg? We decide, on reflection, the best tactic is to own up to having had 'a very small party' / ' a few friends over' and then keep quiet and hope for the best. I can't imagine they will ever guess what went on.

How I meet Conrad in Brighton

On The Road Again...

The circumstances of my first encounter with Conrad are a little shaming and involve a number of complex fabrications that my friend Helena (from school) and I carefully concoct. Helena is one of those cool kids who rebels and achieves at the same time. What makes her even cooler is the fact that she never blows her own trumpet and is naturally modest. Helena says she will be staying at my place for the weekend and I tell my parents I'll be staying with her. Easy, and the oldest trick in the book. On the other hand: Why is no one bothering to check up? But then this is exactly what we want. We have learned to exploit our distracted, pre-occupied parents mercilessly.

Helena and I are off to Brighton for the weekend. I'm not entirely sure why Brighton has been selected as the destination of our choice, but it may be that its growing reputation as the counter cultural capital of the south has singled it out. Helena gives me explicit instructions as to what to say, do and pack in my rucksack. I am to say "We're on the road" if anyone asks even though in fact we will be on the train. I am to show up at the station with my rucksack full of books such as 'On The Road' of course - just to accentuate the point - and some of Leonard Cohen's poetry. I will need to include a Russian author such as Dostoyevsky and something political, say, a manifesto of some sort - Marx, Mao or Trotsky? Bearing in mind that I don't read, anything, ever, this is pushing it a bit - I sincerely hope no one tries to engage me in conversation about my supposed literary tastes or political affiliations - they will be disappointed and I will be found out for the liar I am increasingly becoming. The rucksack contains nothing that is actually useful, such as food, water, Swiss Army penknife or warm, waterproof clothes but this really doesn't matter too much except that it is so heavy with the weight of the books (and expectation too, I guess). I do wonder why being on the road is so important to Helena but she seems to know what she's about and I trust that.

The first part of our escapade is meticulously executed and goes exactly to plan but it doesn't extend quite as far as it might, as we discover upon our arrival.

"What are we going to do?"

'Dunno'

"Have you been to Brighton before?"

'Nope, have you?'

"Nope. D'you know anyone from here?"

'Nope'

"Have you got any money on you?"

'Umm.. not really, a couple of quid I think, somewhere. Have you?'

"No I spent it all on the train fare".

'Oh... Aren't you hungry?'

"Mmm.....YES... starving, haven't eaten since yesterday lunchtime. My stomach is shrinking I'm so bloody hungry!"

'Where're we gonna stay tonight?'

"Dunno, don't keep asking me so many fucking questions! I just have to *think*." Helena's head is bowed forward in intense concentration.

We meander down to the sea, dodging the incoming waves - giggling at the audacity of the scavenging seagulls as they move in on anyone fool enough to be carrying food on them. For a while we're just little kids again messing around on the gravelly beach, chasing each other and the seagulls, chucking stones into the breaking waves. We forget about where we'll be staying, how we'll manage to eat. Gradually the weather moves in and it begins to rain.

The next part of the plan has to be hatched on the hoof wandering aimlessly around the laynes and narrow streets and after sitting it out on the miserable, drizzly promenade, now starving hungry, becoming increasingly foul tempered and falling rapidly and dejectedly out of love with the concept of freedom.

It is exactly at this point, as so often happens when all seems hopeless, that we spot a small group of people who we target to help us out of our predicament. The clothes are a giveaway. A shortish longhaired guy is wearing a top hat, another taller one is wearing the tails part of the outfit, and there's a fair-haired girl perhaps a bit older than us, wrapped up in a Victorian embroidered shawl with tassels which is doing little to keep the vile weather conditions out. A kindred spirit, undoubtedly. Under Helena's instruction and surveillance we stalk them along the laynes whilst figuring out what we're going to say once we've ambushed them. It doesn't take a genius to work out our opening gambit:

"Umm... Hi there. Hi. Hope you don't mind us asking, umm we're looking to score some dope. You haven't got any, have you, by any chance?"

This is fairly outrageous considering we are penniless, underage, pretty much destitute right now and certainly not in a position to buy anything from anyone. We don't bother saying 'We're on the road' now despite the fact it has surreptitiously become an accurate description of our homeless, luxury-free status and one-way ticket lifestyle.

Helena is an atheist but because my major pre-occupation in life has been to find a way to live forever, I'm ever open to the possibility there may be a higher power of some description hiding out somewhere. At this precise moment, he/she/it has made a very spectacular appearance in our miserable lives in the form of these kind people who take us in, feed us and offer us shelter from the metaphorical storm that is gathering force around the periphery of our awareness.

One of the people we meet (the short one with the long hair in the top hat) is Conrad.

Practical Philosophy with Conrad

Tonight I'll be Staying Here with You

There's often been a reticence on my part when it comes to talking honestly about Conrad and his influence at this critical point in my development. Bearing in mind that I am dropping dramatically and rapidly through the net educationally, I show no interest in availing myself of the opportunities inherent in the relative privilege of my upbringing and I am, more worryingly, demonstrating behaviours such as - 'disturbed' and 'delinquent' - the subsequent arrival of Conrad, of course, does absolutely nothing to appease my parents. In fact, I'm surprised they haven't called the police.

Conrad is neither a hobo, nor a vagrant and he has friends at Sussex University. This statement of fact keeps him, in my mind, attached to some semblance of respectability. That this is starting to matter to me is worth wondering about too. I mean, I like edgy but sometimes things get just a little too edgy. Conrad lives way out on the farthest edge. Streetwise is an understatement. He shows me how he keeps hypothermia at bay with a thick layer of newspaper between his skin and his clothing. He lives courtesy of the generosity of friends, students primarily, and customers (he may be a dope dealer - I am beginning to think) yet, he is in the romantic sense, a Free Spirit. He embodies the actual lifestyle Helena and I have aspired to and just been exposed to in these few misery-infused hours in Brighton before, mercifully, we are snatched from the streets by these strangers who are concerned for our heath & safety (well, up to a point).

Yet, without a doubt, as any fool can see, the main thing going for him as far as I can fathom is that Conrad (though not quite in the same league as Ian McShane) is quintessentially Gypsy.

Looking a little like a shorter version of Che Guevara, Conrad is scratching his dark scraggy beard whilst rolling a joint - Red Leb - he says. We're all sitting around the coal fire in the front room in the student accommodation of someone's friend's friend. Jez (the taller guy in the coat tails) has made toast with butter and jam, that is just beautiful beyond description when not a morsel of food has graced our lips for 36 hours. No longer empty and starving, I start thinking about Candace in her big empty castle of a house with the mad mother. Except she's not there anymore - no one knows where she is. Helena reminds me of Candace except with an education and parents who may well be as absent as Candace's. She even looks like Candace being small, and at the moment glossily dark haired (though her hair colour changes on a regular basis). She is far more disinhibited than my own natural shyness and acquired lack of self worth will allow for. Though I suffer this in a multitude of ways, it is also the quality, if you can call it that, that keeps me from going completely off the rails, when I so easily could, and it protects me from veering into physical and psychological danger. This predisposition or trait is something the adults in my life seem entirely unaware of and it's going to come in very useful as a deterrent of sorts.

Conrad decides almost immediately that he would like me to come and live with him, though this is just pure fantasy talk and everyone knows it. Where? Since he doesn't have a home. How? Since neither of us earn any money apart from his bit of dealing and although the make up is helping and I look a fair bit older, I am a child of 13. Excuse me, yes, I am 13. Is he listening and taking this in? Does he realise this? Yes, in a way, sort of. The conversation between us that happens that first weekend around the fire with toast and something to smoke bathes everybody present in a warm, slightly surreal aura of closeness and security. Helena seems to be getting friendly with Jez who is lavishing a fair bit of attention her way. I don't seem to be worried about Conrad taking advantage of my youth - it isn't what this is about, well not quite. There is an attraction to him which is difficult for me to admit because I'm unsure what that might mean. But there is an unwritten code of respect as well, and nothing is going to get taken too far. He is 26 - and an ex wife is floating around somewhere too. None of this looks that great on paper and the more I consider it the worse it sounds. This much I know. Yet paradoxically, I notice right from the start, I feel safe around him.

Something Conrad proposes resonates in me: Maybe I don't he suggests, have to live entirely according to the dictates of those who have unrealistic expectations of me. He elaborates, perhaps it is more a 'State of Mind' that leaves me feeling so unfree as much as it is an actuality, and if I were able to change my state of mind it could make a significant difference to how I feel. Conrad knows all about feeling: He has LOVE and HATE tattooed quite crudely onto the fingers of each hand which indicates to me that he has belonged to a Tribe other than this one in some former incarnation. I wonder where he comes from, what his life has really been about leading up to this day of our meeting and what it is that has hurt so much. I've only just met him but even I can feel the hurt. He'd like to have the HATE removed now but he can't afford to, obviously.

My contact with Conrad will continue on and off for the next three years or so during which time he will find an ingenious solution to the ongoing accommodation problem courtesy of HM Prison, Lewes. This is going to work well for him, and how he deals with this situation contributes philosophically to the construction of my own set of inner values. I will explain:

Con is frequently arrested for minor offences which is part and parcel of 'the lifestyle'. He gets nicked, shoplifting really useless things, for example Smarties, which to me seems a bit of a wasted opportunity. He is not particularly practical. There are a few cannabis related offences though nothing too extreme. He can rarely pay the fines so whilst conveniently banged up he writes to me, letters which I find on the doormat on my way out of the door to school some mornings. There is no subtlety about HM Prison blue-lined notepaper - it has its identity stamped in bold unashamed letters all over it. No escaping that Someone Is Writing To You From PRISON. No discretion whatsoever. And.... No getting away from the fact that the major distraction in class now comes in the form of these letters, some of which get confiscated and which I hope are being read and the contents therein, taken on board:

Conrad writes to me in beautiful descriptive language detailing the Gothic arches and structures of his current abode and the complex history of his relationship with it. He finds a poetic means of bringing to life in verse, for example, the birdsong he identifies, as he listens for it at dusk or at sunrise from behind the bars of his small window as he sits in contemplative thought. His words are flowing and free, his demeanour is optimistic and light despite his physical incarceration. His spirit is lifted by the dawn chorus that brings with it hope of his release each new day yet he recognises that true freedom resides within....... ad infinitum (sorry Con, I don't mean to sound quite so cynical - I'm just trying to make a point).

Meanwhile I am moodily, scratchily skulking around in a bitter nihilistic underworld that is the prison of my own tortured mind and my grey, miserable life at school. I am locked into an intolerable, sadistic regime that has been prescribed for me entirely and completely without my will or consent to which I am legally bound for a minimum sentence of at least another 3 years. *Point made.*

Childhood is Hell...

(...and adolescence is... hell as well and I'm still only 13)

We've Gotta Get Out of This Place...

As you can clearly see, I am desperate to grow up. I cannot abide the petty restrictions of childhood and adolescence, for that matter. I am mystified by these idyllic stories I keep hearing and the associated memories and pictures that people keep coming up with. Have they been brainwashed? Who are these fantasists? *Childhood is hell.* You have no control over anything and the expectations placed upon you are entirely unrealistic. No one has the faintest idea who you are or takes the important things that genuinely matter seriously. And those people who say their schooldays were the best? Who are they kidding?

It's like having Locked-In Syndrome. You can sense all this weird, secret stuff going on around you but you cannot coherently explain it or express it. If you ever dare to try you're met with patronising glances or supercilious facial expressions and sometimes, aggression. Or worse still, sent to a boarding school or a shrink.

Let's get real here. There's no looking back to a glorious earlier time either - no 'golden glow' of childhood let alone infantile bliss. It never happened - wake up! There's just a mass of hormones and chemical processes wreaking havoc in your immature body and brain, forcing you to fight impulses you have absolutely no control over and to cap it, you are surrounded by people who are utterly clueless and with countless bizarre and unresolved issues of their own.

I suddenly realise what I am saying! Good God! For the first time ever I think I've found an ally in old Sigmund! I am in shock. Truly, deeply in shock. Bloody hell! Who saw that coming?

My New Shrink & the Bodysnatchers

(still 13, still getting into trouble)

Please Don't Let me be Misunderstood

I've been allocated a brand new shrink though this statement is not quite true. She is the wife of a close colleague of my father who I've spotted at dinner parties round here once or twice. So not really brand new because I already know her. I'm free-associating and linking this woman to my mother's exhausting and neurotic pre dinner party routine. As I let my mind wander, as you do with free-association, I see she has indirectly caused my mother to suffer. This is a hopeless start. I know this shrink already socially and it seems I don't much like her or what she's done to someone I dearly love..........

Of course I could just be avoiding the very real issues that I'm here to discuss with her. Ok, might as well spit it out then: *I've recently been arrested and locked up in a police cell for the night and I doubt it's been anything remotely like Conrad's experience of prison. It isn't funny.*

My new shrink has a name a bit like Abby. That's what we'll be calling her. She's a member of the *non-speaking' school of psychoanalysis.*

"Do I have to tell you all about it? (I'm speaking to Abby, who nods) Yes, alright then, here goes:

"I really thought when Mum and Dad got to the police station everything would be fine. I didn't expect them to gang up against me and get all smarmy with the police. Never in a million, billion years did I think that! Aren't you going to say anything, aren't you shocked?" (Abby is motionless)

"Ok, I'll carry on and tell you the whole story from the beginning: We just wanted to see what was going on in Trafalgar Square. Yes, it was evening but it was broad daylight, you know its summer, isn't it? I went with my friend (Jessica) - did the usual thing, she said she'd be at mine and I'd be going round to hers. We both like the poetry that's been read a lot at the moment and there's a lot of interesting people, brilliant music and things happening now. It's really exciting and new. Sometimes you just want to feel part of something you can relate to, sort of on your wave length for a change. Don't you? I mean I do. It's not such a crime is it?" (I wait for Abby to respond. Nothing.)

"You don't look all that shocked but I haven't got to the part that got me into trouble yet. Should I carry on?" (She nods.)

"Ok. If you look like me (barefoot, scruffy jeans, crazy hair etc) and you hang out with your similarly dressed friends, you know, these days the police often stop and check you out? They 'book' you. Meaning write down your name in their book although you haven't committed a crime so they can't actually do anything else. Didn't you know that? God, It happens all the time! Round here in Hampstead especially. It all depends on how you look, like I said. Well, I didn't want Mum and Dad to know about this because sometimes I'm not where I say I'm going to be. It's not a big deal, ok. So when they (the police) have been stopping us recently locally and asking us for our names for their 'book' I made one up, made up a false one. Get it?"

Silence from Abby.

"You look confused. You still haven't said a word. It's not that bloody complicated!

"Right. That night in Trafalgar Square we were hanging around waiting for someone to play some music or read some poetry, sort of thing. These guys came up to us who we quickly got rid of because they seemed quite, I don't know, creepy. Yes, creepy. It wasn't a problem at all. We ignored them and they buggered off. But then the police who must have been watching this and coming to some weird conclusion in their warped minds, came up to us and took Jessica to one side of the Square and me to the other and asked us all about ourselves *and each other.* She gave them my real name, but I used the one I made up.

"That was it! Bloody hell! Should have seen them snap into action, like bleeding robots. Next thing we are being dragged off to Canon Row police station for "interrogation". So my actual crime so far is giving them a false name. When they asked why, I said exactly why. My parents think I'm somewhere else, and that is all. But then they kept going on about '*loitering with intent*' whatever that's supposed to mean?" (Abby's eyes are widening very slightly now.)

"Shit, ok. God this is hard. They took away our belongings. I mean I had a bag with school books in it, for Chrissake. I also had pyjamas in case I ended up staying at Jessica's. They made a big bloody deal of that. You should have seen them! They separated us so I didn't see Jessica again that night. Then they took my belt off my jeans and threw me in a prison cell..

"Now you look shocked - I can see it in your face. It's ok I haven't got to the really nasty bit yet even." (Abby's eyes are now very wide open.)

"Shall I carry on? They didn't know we were only 13. They really didn't. It seemed to make things a whole lot worse. First they accuse us of the '*loitering with intent*' thing and then they start talking about putting us '*under care and protection*' when they find out we're quite young. It just escalated. While I was in the cell every half hour or so a bunch of policemen would come in and sort of leer and jeer at me. They made jokes like "what do you want to do when you grow up then? Ha, ha...." I just said the first thing that came into my head 'I want to be an interior designer' "Fine way you're going about it" Sneer, sneer and ridicule ridicule. Then they'd march out again. Have you ever been banged up in a police cell when you haven't done anything wrong? And you're only 13? (Abby shakes her head wisely in a contemplative manner) No, I didn't think so."

"Ok, so this song and dance went on for a bit longer and then a policewoman came to get me. She and this policeman took me into a side room for interrogation. They were quite threatening. They started to ask me some very personal questions in a very heavy way. Like had I ever taken any drugs? Of course I'm not an idiot and I said no. They asked about whether I knew anyone who did and where they got it from. And exactly who and what and where. I still had my wits about me and I was thinking about my friends Candace, Helena, Conrad but of course I said nothing. Still with me?" (An Abby nod.)

"Next the policewoman asked me to describe to her in graphic detail *'exactly how far I'd gone with* a *boy. Exactly what I did, what he did*. When, where, who etc. I was absolutely terrified and it was like I felt I had no choice but to tell them the truth. I didn't say who anyone was, that would have been so awful, but I did say what I'd done. Thing is I've had a bit of experience (like everyone I know, come on, we've all got a bit touchy feely with each other at parties and things) but I didn't expect my few measly fumblings to be seen as so disgusting or strange. The policewoman shouted at me 'Have you no pride in your body?' I thought she was going to hit me. She raised her hand. What business is it of hers what I feel about my own body? But then, and this is the bit that really bothered me she said they were going to have me examined by a police surgeon to see if I was still a virgin. I was thinking - Shit! Can they do that!? Then they shoved me back in the cell and I waited for hours and hours for Mum and Dad to get there and rescue me."

(Abby now has a genuinely compassionate look on her face)

"Yeah I know, sorry, can I have a tissue, please? I wasn't sure who'd get to me first, my folks or the police surgeon. Well about 3 in the morning my parents arrive. I mean they only went to the theatre so I'm not sure why it took them so long. I was so unbelievably glad to see them.

"I felt totally relieved until something really horrible happened. They started to side with the police, agreeing with them and looking horrified at my evil deeds - especially the thing about how far I'd gone with a boy, which was utterly ridiculous. I had the feeling they would have handed me over to the bloody police surgeon if he'd been there. You'd think the police were their best bloody friends." I pause because I'm choking up a bit.

"Really, I felt so utterly betrayed by them. I was speechless. They took me home in the car in complete silence so I felt like a criminal. When we got back they ran a cold bath and made me get in it. I think with my clothes on? Can't even remember properly. My mother looked so upset and almost crying but I didn't know why or what was so awful about me. I mean who were these people for God's sake? It was like my normal loving cool parents had been taken over by some other super straight life force. Like something in a movie. Body Snatchers. Completely out of character. I mean what on earth happened to their so called liberal values? And also what's their issue with authority all of a sudden? I feel furious.

"One last bit, shall go on? Yes?" (Abby nods.)

"The next day they went through my wardrobe and threw out lots of my clothes. They grounded me for a month. Vetted all my friends. Made me change my hair. My mother started chaperoning me to any parties or social get togethers. It was so embarrassing. Oh yeah and my parents specifically asked the police not to tell the school and they promised not too. Well, guess what? On Monday I was called to Miss B's office (ancient headmistress) and she had been written to by the bloody police. Whose a liar now? But what surprised me was that old Miss B was really nice to me. I mean really kind, sympathetic. Much nicer than Mum and Dad. That really cut me up. Can you believe it?" Sort of shrug from Abby, kindly delivered.

"Aren't you wondering what happened to Jessica? (An Abby nod) D'you know, her parents were really cool. I mean *really* cool. No problem. But Miss B was not so nice to her. Not sure I understand that. Can I have another tissue or two to take with me?" (She passes me a new box of tissues in a kindly sort of way.)

"Thanks and thanks a lot, really, for listening to all this stuff." I feel genuinely grateful she's stuck with the story. "Do you still want to see me next week after all I've told you?" (I can't determine quite what the expression on Abby's face is telling me but she's looking at me in a sympathetic way, I think?)

I don't know what happened next but for reasons unbeknownst to me I didn't stay long in therapy with Abby. Was I too much for her (as I feared I might be - naturally) or did the friendship/ colleagueship with my father get in the way? But then she never said much so I never found out.

Stubbing Cigarettes out with My Bare Feet

By the end of that summer the soles of my feet are so hardened by all the exposure they've been getting I can now painlessly put cigarettes out with them. I am proud of this for some inexplicable reason. It feels like a real achievement. Definitely something for the CV.

Maybe I'm developing a hardened crust too so I don't get so hurt by the things I keep stepping on and tripping over? No, I don't think so, not really, not at all.

I've just heard that Candace has gone off to live with 'a boyfriend'. She's a bit young, but who knows what the real story is. The house up the road seems not just to be empty but now it's boarded up too. I don't know what's happened to Bette Davis and the labradors. I wish Candace had dropped in to say goodbye at least.

Pharmaceuticals & Us

Everybody's Got Something to Hide Except for Me & My Monkey

As you might have gathered, I had been failing academically in quite spectacular fashion. By the time I was approaching 14 the downward trajectory was unstoppable. It might have been effects of the early cannabis use on my underdeveloped adolescent brain or that in combination with other inner demons and processes. I struggled to keep my fragmenting mind focussed when it wanted desperately to take flight via the first available exit. I wrote poetry and lyrics secretly at my school desk and identified the cloud formations shapeshifting up in the skies beyond the classroom window - 'mmm there's a wild horse up there, or maybe it's Pegasus? That's a stunningly elegant swan, oh but now it's turning into a fat fluffy duck. The duck is breaking up now..... there it goes......bye bye duck' etc. I watched and drifted with the overhead menagerie, oblivious to the lesson being taught and carried on with the lyric writing. I found it humiliating that some of my peers, even the more rebellious contemporaries, were able to do their individuating and rebelling whilst still maintaining their educational track record, like the supremely intelligent Helena for example. Personally I found it impossible. It was not a matter of not wanting to, it was a matter of not being able to. But the shame that came with this incapacity drove me to pretend I didn't care, when I cared deeply.

On the other hand I was a popular kid and had plenty of friendships at school and a life outside of it, so a thread of optimism about my future, however it might turn out, co existed next to the other reality. I'd also starting writing some interesting songs.

During the summers at school when the most important exams were being taken I was often asleep or fighting a losing battle to stay conscious, being allergic across the spectrum : animal vegetable mineral : - flowers, trees, tomatoes, the sun, chrome, nickel, dust, feathers, cats, dogs, horses, guinea pigs, my own laughter sometimes (provoking an allergic asthmatic reaction) and probably kangaroos had I been tested for them - but the worst offender by miles was the dreaded grass pollen. At the time my mother, who shared this affliction and therefore sympathised, was experimenting with various drug treatments to alleviate the wheezing, itching, streaming and general misery. She had never been allergic to anything before she set foot upon these fertile spore-infused shores. In SA they didn't have the same high strength super potent pollen, clearly.

Being a doctor she had access to some of the newer more experimental drugs. After a number of trials we collectively agreed the one that worked best was a yellow and white killer of a pill called Triaminic *. It produced bizarre visual distortions and disturbances, before anaesthetizing the brain and body into total submission. Just half a killer pill would temporarily knock out the effects of the allergies whilst knocking everything else out in the process. The manufacturers still had a way to go getting the dosage right.

Another drug I tried courtesy of my mother's research was called Triluden** and it made you sick as dog if you drank alcoholic under its influence. My father should have been on this one.

Pharmaceuticals and us: The medicine cabinet at home became the envy of our friends, particularly when it was stocked up with Mandrax - Dad's favourite sleeping pill but also a desirable party accessory of that era: a different kind of high but probably used like ecstasy is these days. Half a Mandy would get you feeling 'drunk' without the physical symptoms that accompanied actual drinking. Just enough to bring on the right kind of high. The detrimental factor was, in my limited experience, the stultifying depression that descended like a suffocating grey veil after a weekend of Mandy use, which probably accounts for its short-lived popularity (and that it was discontinued - banned, in fact). This my friend Georgina and I discovered after a solid weekend of secret Mandy use upstairs at home. I wanted to kill myself (well, for a short while).

There was also the question of the local Chemists. An unholy alliance existed between my parents, the pharmacist and their compliant GP that ensured access 365 days a year to whatever drugs were required or desired. The pharmacist supplied and later, after the event, the GP would write the prescription under orders from which ever parent. I would be sent to collect the various drug packages, which I was more than happy to do because I could put whatever else I wanted on their account. I had acquired a drawer full of mascaras, Wella hair conditioners, kohl eye liners, Miners White Lipstick and I gladly fulfilled my duties as their drugs runner and accepted the mule's reward that came with the role.

Later on there was a similar arrangement with Arthur Cooper, the off licence, where we put our packets of Player's No. 6 on the account in return for purchasing and bringing home bottles of vodka for dad when he could no longer get there under his own steam.

Footnotes:

- *Triominic - This medication may impair your thinking or reactions. Be careful if you drive or do anything that requires you to be alert. (Like stay awake at school? KL)
- **Triludan - The Government's drug control agency is closely monitoring the country's most popular hay fever treatment after reports that it could cause a heart attack if taken with other drugs or by people with damaged livers. The company that makes the drug, Triludan, which is available over the counter has written to all GPs and pharmacists reinforcing its warning advice. The Department of Health has also issued its own public warning to users.

- - - - - - - - - - - - - -

Hello Kit

I'm a little concerned. I suggested a couple of A4 sheets for your biography ahead of our working together and now you've sent me this. Clearly you are writing something substantially longer (a book?). At least this is how it appears from the last 'instalment' you have emailed me. However, that is not where my greatest concerns lie: there are historical childhood safeguarding issues that clearly have never been addressed, alongside the various substance abuse incidents that feature throughout your adolescence. In fact, I was wondering if you might have been rather heavily under the influence of any such substances yourself in recent times as the feel (breezy, almost dangerously flippant at times?) of your writing might indicate? I would suggest, if we are no longer going to be meeting in the foreseeable future, that you contact your GP as a first port of call if you feel you are struggling to cope. I trust however, as you yourself are a therapist, that you will make sure you are in touch with the relevant professionals should you require additional support.

With kind regards
Dr Maelstrum

PS strictly off the record: Bloody hell Kit Lindfield you had an exciting time when you were 13. I wish my own restrictive and quite frankly, love-starved childhood had been half as exciting.

I'm beginning to wish I'd met you back then (perhaps scrub that last sentence).

- - - - - - - - - - - - - - -

Hi Dr Maelstrum

At last! I thought you'd died or something. Why the silence until now? Where on earth have you been hiding all these weeks? Actually I'm doing fine ever since I started this writing thing - your idea, if you remember! Things are definitely looking up and 'I would suggest' (to use your phraseology) that you ease up a little on all that superego stuff. Give yourself a break! Chill, why don't you?

Hope all is well in your world (?)
Kit

PS Strictly off the record - what on earth was going on in your grim childhood then? I guess I shouldn't ask but I can't resist. Anyway back to the writing.......

Songwriting...

While My Guitar Gently Weeps

... Started to become important when I was about 12, but its origins went further back to primary school. I'd always made up melodies - when I was around 7 or 8 and played the recorder at school I would tootle away for hours in my bedroom and invent simple tunes and then harmonies for a second recorder. Our parents took us to see the musical, Oliver, a little later on. A love song the character Nancy sang stuck in my mind. Quite spontaneously and almost unconsciously I found myself plagiarising this song, borrowing from it and then making up my own version of it, lyrically and melodically, and the process evolved. Ezra was very encouraging being a musician of sorts himself - he played jazz piano and could pick up a melody intuitively. The myth propagated in the family was that had he not become a shrink he would have pursued a career as a jazz pianist. One day he taught me *'There's a small hotel, by that wishing well'* on the piano, and later he showed me the chords for the brooding, original version of Summertime which I still hear in my head to this day. I remember him saying how often people don't play it right, they miss out on the melancholic slow bell toll of a rhythm with its alternating minor chords as it starts.

I sensed that as my father played the piano it drew him back to some other earlier version of himself. Another life that could have or might have once been a possibility, that had been set adrift and abandoned way back and long ago. It felt deeply, poignantly sad to me and yet not indulgent in any way. As if it might be connecting him once again to something he could not bear to lose. And I would surreptitiously listen in on the stairs above as he improvised on the piano downstairs.

Ezra's support and enthusiasm for my songwriting almost got me a foot in the door of the music establishment early on when I was 14. I was invited by a publisher via a personal contact of his to come and play my songs. He liked one of them enough to want to publish it or I think sell it on. It was in the early days of Joni Mitchell and in the dying days of an earlier 60's folk music scene. I bore an uncanny physical similarity to Mary Hopkin (long blondish hair, shy downwards gaze) who vanished into obscurity after one hit song around that time. It never happened of course, the publishing deal, but I felt something I did that I cared about had been recognised.

It was the 'creative thing' as we called it, that linked my father and I. It wasn't only about music. In those moments we could see beyond the complicated adolescent daughter / father relationship just for a while, and appreciate something as equals. I knew he wished only good things for me in my music making or arts projects - where ever my creativity chose to take me - and he recognised how painful my lack of confidence was becoming - how much it scuppered my capacity to perform. I was desperate not to give damn what other people thought, just like he didn't give a damn most of the time, but I did and there was nothing much I could do to shift it.

Yet much as there was encouragement, my father also had this uncanny way of undermining any tenuous feelings of self confidence. Like, for example, when I became interested in playing the saxophone and with my parents' help found a secondhand instrument in a music shop in Denmark Street. Any excitement was dissipated pretty much from the start. Almost as soon as I'd brought it home and taken it out of its case Ezra started making comments and observations in the usual Freudian vein, such as *'Mmmm... the saxophone is becoming your penis extension, I think'*..... Yes, really. It was as if he couldn't stop himself. A kind of psychoanalytical Tourettes Syndrome. I felt like screaming **'Fucking hell, Dad, just keep a lid on the bloody diagnostics, won't you!!'** Didn't he get that? Didn't he see that it's difficult enough for adolescents and their highly self conscious relationship with their weirdly morphing bodies, and that his comments were so grossly insensitive? Apparently not, not even with the best training in the developed world. Yet somehow, I knew he was only doing what he always did in the name of attempting to 'help'.

The songs though, irrespective of all else, wrote themselves and had a life of their own. That's how it felt, and I found myself in an internal conversation with perhaps a wiser, more friendly part of my own internal world. If there was a feeling waiting to be expressed it would be revealed to me through the writing; if I didn't know what was going on in my inner world, the song would draw it out in images and phrases. Often I had absolutely no idea what I was writing about. I began to understand what people mean when they talk about 'channelling'. No, it isn't some weird mystic thing, more a feeling that something is coming through you rather than originating within you. Some song lyrics to this day, make no sense whatsoever but it doesn't matter. When I wrote I felt contented and at peace with the world and everything in it. A bit like as in the dreaming process, the disconnected fragments found a way of knitting and weaving themselves together without effort.

The Black Limo & the Ocean Liner

Oh Lord, won't you buy me a Mercedes Benz?

In the springtime just before my 14th birthday my parents decided we were to take a holiday in Israel. Some ancestral family land had been sold and for complicated financial reasons the proceeds couldn't easily be shipped over here so the only solution was for us to spend it over there. I have to admit, I was not exactly enthusiastic. In fact, that is a gross understatement. Being deeply uncomfortable being Jewish, looking Jewish, the last place I felt like going to was Israel where I would be affirming an identity I was ambivalent about in the first place.

Recently whilst minding my own business standing on the platform at Golders Green tube station a strange man had walked up to me, aggressively stared me in the face and simply stated in accusatory fashion 'You're a Jew, aren't you?' Cornered, I felt I had no choice but to say "Yes?" My accuser walked off muttering something like **and you look like one too.** It never occurred to me that I could have told him where to get off. Or that I might have turned away and ignored him completely. Instead in that single moment the flimsily constructed denial of my roots came falling away. I knew physically, viscerally, the age old scent of persecution and recognised the inescapable truth of my heritage. And I loathed with a vengeance, wearing this heritage so obviously. It was like being caught naked in public. Soon after I started to re connect to dreams I'd been having for years. Dreams I'd been doing my best to push back into unconsciousness. A common theme was finding myself in the wrong place at the wrong time. Often in the dream state I was about to be punished and sometimes executed for nothing more than that. I had done nothing, hadn't committed a crime or a particular offence, my transgression simply being the fact of who I was by virtue of my birth and my blood. In my waking reflections I considered changing my name, my identity, to something, anything, less obviously Jewish. And I considered changing my appearance too.

In contemplating our imminent trip the inner voice was insisting, pleading 'please don't make me' - that is, go to Israel, though that statement could easily be applied to the contents of the persecutory dream scenarios I had failed to banish. I did not want to face my own fears.

We took a train across Italy and boarded a cruise liner at the port in Genoa to sail to Haifa. My parents, noticing my anxiety and trepidation consoled me with promises of visits to an artists' colony, thinking that might help me have a sense of connectedness to something non-threatening. I noticed they too seemed uncomfortable. Neither of my parents had been to Israel before and it was only a year since the 6 day war. Also we were to spend these few weeks in the company of my maternal grandfather, Aaron and my great aunt Sara both of whom were widowed and had found companionship with each other.

We spent 5 days on the ocean liner stopping off in places en route such as Rhodes and Ephesus. My father was more used to being on ships as his refusal to fly meant sailing on the Union Castle from Southampton to Cape Town every few years to see his parents. This entailed a 2 week ocean voyage each way, where he entertained himself playing cards with the old ladies (his description, not mine) on the upper deck. My mother and Jake would fly out from Heathrow and meet him at the port as he disembarked, bored, exhausted and sick of card games with elderly ladies.

This time en famille there were enough distractions once over the sea sickness to keep us all relatively amused. I found a dog eared copy of a James Bond novel down in the stuffy cabin, and it was the closest I'd ever come to reading a whole book that wasn't full of ponies and gymkhanas or stolen Leonard Cohen poems. There were a few day trips to keep the boredom at bay and other attempts at entertaining the passengers: from the sublime - wandering through the ancient site of Ephesus with my mother who it turned out, was a sensationally well informed tour guide. To the utterly ridiculous - bingo each afternoon on board in the ballroom and the occasional excruciating after dinner dance.

Once docked in Haifa we were met by an enormous black limousine plus chauffeur/tour guide.

My father looked aghast, and more so when my grandfather and great aunt stepped out of it smiling and welcoming. My grandfather Aaron was tall, bald headed and almost charismatic with pronounced cheek bones and sculpted facial features. He had lost a kidney as a young man but despite this, prided himself on his fitness and resilience. He swam everyday in the Muizenberg sea apparently and put his good health and full set of unfilled teeth down in part to his love of chewing stale white bread. The other slightly odd thing about Grandpa Aaron was his insistence that he should sleep without pillows and he swore that that was a major health benefit in itself. My great aunt Sara was a tiny angular woman with a grey bun, so slight in physique that she'd once been blown onto a railway track and had to be dramatically rescued. Once when in London visiting she had handed me an ancient silver bracelet with strange hieroglyphics welded onto the body of it. She was mystified as to what they might mean and asked me to investigate on her behalf. It didn't take long. They were the signs of the zodiac and I wondered how it had come to be in her possession. Back home rummaging around I had discovered ancient photos of her looking mysterious, longhaired and bohemian, wearing embroidered gypsy shawls rather like the ones I was appropriating for my own wardrobe. She was sister to my grandfather's deceased wife Rose who had been a good ten years older than him.

Aaron and Sara had made their way from Cape Town to be

with us in Israel. The limousine and chauffeur were part of the deal. Everywhere we went it came too. It stalked us like a shiny black shark. Even when we chose to walk it skulked along just behind us. Sometimes its presence was threatening depending on where we were. The Arabic street bazaars and winding market roads (of the recently occupied parts of east Jerusalem that had been taken by the Israelis the year before our arrival) were not the most comfortable places to turn up looking affluently western. There were bullet holes in the crumbling walls of the buildings and our conspicuous presence courtesy of the black shark didn't instil confidence. We shouldn't have been there, we had no right, at least that is how it felt to me.

I became aware of danger in a sexualised sense when I was grabbed by the arm one morning wandering in east Jerusalem and dragged into the back of a market stall selling sheepskin coats. I found myself being fitted up and touched up all at the same time whilst inhaling the pungent aroma of old sheep, thus ensuring that old sheep and inappropriate sexual occurrences were forever linked in my memory banks. This vendor seemed to have about 4 pairs of hands. They were everywhere imaginable in the space of about 30 seconds. He'd clearly had plenty of practice.

On this trip one of the surprising elements became the nature of the relationship with my father - the rebel in him gladly it seemed, colluding with the rebel in me. I couldn't work out whether his rebellion on this occasion had been triggered by his father in law's presence and the restrictiveness of the situation or by simply, awkwardly being in Israel, or perhaps by both. Whilst my mother held the dutiful daughter/ mother role, my father and I sneaked around like a pair of wayward, guilty adolescents escaping after dinner to smoke behind pillars in no smoking areas and hang about in coffee bars in Tel Aviv. My father was quick to notice if there was any male attention heading in my direction and seemed perfectly at ease with this, in fact, almost encouraging of it.

One evening out in the Bathsheba desert we ate our candle lit dinner en famille whilst a jazz band played in the starlit palm tree courtyard of the hotel. My father seemed to get it into his head that I should make off with the saxophone player. It started as a family joke, though his fantasy loosely became a kind of experiment to see if I could attract the opposite sex. I could, sometimes. The problem became what to do once I had. Sex became the unlikely sub text of the trip. I wondered vaguely and occasionally what my father's investment in my capacity to attract might be about. But I didn't question it too much then. One anomaly occurred to me though. Those bodysnatched parents of mine who had been so aghast at the sexual fumblings I'd revealed to the police on my Trafalgar Square arrest a few months earlier, bore little resemblance to the set of parents I was currently hanging around with.

Sam and I spent some of our time wandering around the beaches in Eilat where we had briefly stopped, in search of a smoke. We scored one evening courtesy of an American Peace

Corps worker called Chas who sat with us on the sand smoking and romanticising about the starry night-lit horizon in what seemed like a florid, cheesy outpouring. Utterly out of our heads neither Sam nor I could hold back our hysterical giggling. It was ok, our new friend got the joke and when Sam walked from the beach back to the motel, he and I stayed and watched the waves for a while. He wanted to kiss me. I let him but didn't like the hardness of his tongue. We were biding our time 'til our release, albeit from differing obligations, and aside from the texture of his kiss this wasn't such a bad way of going about it.

The next day we were off somewhere else. I barely kept track since we were doing a lightening tour, this peculiar scruffy bunch that we were, stuffed into the ostentatious limo like unlikely, sweaty and bedraggled minor aristocracy after a very heavy night out. It was just plain weird.

Sometime in the middle of all of this I turned 14. It seemed a significantly more substantial number than 13. I was now a proper fully fledged teenager according to the sorts of magazines I was currently reading.

We eventually passed through Ein Hod, the artists' colony my parents had imagined I would relate to, where I bought myself a chunky minimalist silver and onyx ring in one of the studios on the outskirts of the village. My father fell for and acquired a huge, frantic, oil pastel drawing of a man's face, full of pathos with deep, hollowed out eye sockets. I wondered if it looked like he felt.

Our final stop was the port in Haifa. That afternoon in the botanical gardens, knowing we were heading homeward later that evening, something inside at last gave me permission to open my eyes to this strange land that I was supposed to have a connection with. I didn't, that is, feel connected, but oddly and unexpectedly I felt sad. Or was it more about saying goodbye to Aaron and Sara, generationally dislocated, possibly unsettled too by this visit to the alleged 'homeland' and, I suspected, desperate to get back to the familiarity of Cape Town? Whatever its origins, the sadness lingered 'til we'd said our goodbyes to all, seen the back of the stalking black limousine and boarded the ship.

Homeward Bound (I wish I was....)

I was glad to be going home, though we still had a 5 day voyage on the liner to Genoa before the last leg on a sleeper train northbound back through Europe.

On the first or second evening, I can't remember exactly, I met Davide. Davide was 18 and sailing back to Marseilles with his family. We met at a dance on board - we both noticed each other shuffling self consciously across the floorboards to music that wasn't exactly our first choice, trying to look as if we weren't there with our parents and siblings. Davide was proverbially tall, dark and handsome. I was of course, flattered by his interest. We wandered round the ship together attempting to converse courtesy of my lousy French and his equally dubious English. We somehow managed. In between the day trips on various stop overs we gladly hung around together. It was kind of easy and non demanding.

On my last night before disembarking at Genoa (Davide and his family were staying on 'til Marseilles the day after) we decided to go exploring. It felt daring. We found our way to the bridge where we met the 'second-in-command' (I will be calling him s-i-c from now on) who undoubtedly had a proper title but I could not remember what it was. An imposing, white haired, pot bellied man of about 60 in full naval uniform, he was uncommonly friendly and accommodating inviting us to explore the crew's quarters, the galleys and the areas behind the scenes normally hidden from the paying passengers. He then offered us use of his cabin since he would be on duty for the rest of the night and have no need of it himself. Of course we graciously accepted.

His 'suite' was vast and utterly luxurious compared to our cramped, claustrophobic cabins in the cheapest, darkest part of the ship. We were invited to eat and drink whatever we felt like, fruit, various wines, the entire contents of his fridge, had this been what we wanted. I wasn't quite sure what was motivating such an act of generosity, nor did I question it. We poured ourselves a small amount of something alcoholic from his cabinet and mixed it with pineapple juice. Then we hung around kissing and messing around fairly innocently on the huge bed pretending to be upmarket first class passengers. It felt like an adventure and a memorable way of saying goodbye to each other since I would be leaving first thing in the morning when the ship sailed into port at Genoa. As it was getting late, aware of the fact my parents would soon notice my absence, I went to the bathroom to straighten myself up and run my fingers through my haystack hair before making an appearance back with the family. Whilst in this bathroom I thought I heard people speaking together, or whispering, but the noise of the ship's engine obscured anything coherent so I dismissed it.

I was on the loo when the door was flung open and I found myself staring up at the naval uniform of Mr S-i-c looming above me. I was totally horrified and grabbed my crumpled jeans from around my ankles yanking them up as fast as humanly possible. He came lurching forward towards me trying to grab hold of me and engulf me in his portly and hairy arms. I instinctively pulled a towel down from the rail and found myself flicking it in his direction like a whip in a feeble attempt to keep him at bay. I was stunned. Almost dissociated as if I wasn't entirely in my body but thinking '*Oh shit, how the hell do I get out of this?*' Then he got hold of my wrist and yanked me towards him trying to kiss me. I managed by force and a fair bit of kicking to extricate myself from his grasp and escape out of the bathroom back into the bedroom. I was expecting to find Davide. He wasn't there. I made a rush for the door that lead out into the corridor. My hand was shaking so much at first I thought this was why I couldn't open it. I had no grip. I was thinking literally '*Get a grip, for god's sake!*' But in fact the door had been locked. My frustrated tormentor started chasing me around the room begging me to, at the very least, give him a blow job, since I guess he was beginning to doubt that he'd get what he really wanted. I thought I might throw up. Next he went for the old sob story, how very lonely life was at sea as if this would have made me more compliant and accommodating. The rising panic eventually reached a tipping point and I started to cry. If I had appeared older, and I probably had, at this point I regressed to a kid of about 10 years old. I had run out of ideas and his relentless approach was becoming increasingly difficult to evade.

Perhaps my hysterical regression to this whimpering, shaking child scared him. Eventually, he angrily unlocked the door and I tumbled and lurched out of his cabin into the corridor. He then slammed it shut aggressively behind him and locked it from inside.

In the corridor I found Davide sitting on the floor with his back against the wall, his elbows resting on his knees, looking up. Then he smiled. I suddenly got it. That was the deal. We had use of S-i-c's suite and then he had been promised use of me. All conveniently, neatly arranged by Davide. I was the trade off. The words in my head went something like *'You fucking, fucking creep!'* but I found myself utterly unable to speak.

Being shaken and disorientated I relied on Davide to get us back to our quarters since I was too distraught to navigate my own way out of the complex mish mash of hallways and corridors - this underworld deep in the belly of this stinking ship. I wished I hadn't been in need of his help in any way. There were no words spoken between us - absolutely none, nothing.

At breakfast it was similar as I sat with my family. I imagined never wanting to speak again. A proliferation of conflicting feelings log jammed themselves in my consciousness. The inner conversation was as relentless as the outer conversation was non existent: There was the shame, the sense of betrayal, the genuinely terrifying flashbacks, the various 'what ifs' passing through my mind. Yet despite all of this there were the vestiges of attachment nevertheless to this person who had no interest in my well being whatsoever. I was flooded with the utter disbelief that I could even consider feelings of attachment to the dreaded Davide, but there they were in all their blatant, sickening glory. What else remained but to loathe myself for my weakness, my clinging, repulsive neediness. It made me hate my own blood and bones. It made me want to turn viciously against my own nature. Never at any point did it enter my head to tell my parents what had happened. I suddenly got why no one tells. There is always a pervading sense of culpability, of guilt. I was in the wrong place at the wrong time with the wrong person and that was my fault, my choice and my mistake. It made any possibility of revelation a complete non starter.

When we disembarked later that morning in Genoa Davide didn't bother to show up. Why would he? But he showed up in my thoughts all the way home across Europe on the sleeper train and stuck around for a while once we were back in London. He still had a small piece of something of mine in his possession in the form of my silver and onyx ring, which he had point blank refused to return.

- - - - - - - - - - - - - -

Hi Kit

I wasn't intending to comment on the section you've just sent to me, but I had to say something. How on earth did you manage to attract so many psychologically compromised individuals into your life? How is it that trouble follows you everywhere you go? However, I am truly sorry you were on the receiving end of so much shoddy and abusive behaviour. It makes me wonder if there were any redeeming people around you at all? Someone possibly who had your best interests at heart? Other experiences to balance out these appalling incidents? Have a think about it.

Kind regards
Dr Maelstrum

PS off the record: Still despite the obviously traumatic episodes, you clearly had a wildly exciting time! My own biography seems pale and insubstantial next to yours. I'm starting to feel rather envious. The most daring I ever got was at the university debating club dinner where I first experienced getting a little tipsy. The next day I was wracked with shame and foreboding believing I had behaved in a thoroughly unacceptable manner. If my father (headmaster, old school variety) had seen me in such a disinhibited state I would never have survived the humiliation. As for my mother …...... actually I won't go there just now. Apologies for the disclosure.

- - - - - - - - - - - - - -

Hi Dr Maelstrum

Thanks for the comments - you've jogged my memory
so have a read of the next bit if you've got time
what with your busy schedule etc.

Best
Kit

PS You seem to have quite a few unresolved issues
yourself - I do hope you've got someone to talk
these things through with? I could put you in
touch with a colleague who I think you'd get on
well with. Let me know.

The German Connection

Toward the end of 1968 Christa arrived. Christa was 17 and the sister of a German left wing student activist in Hamburg. Christa was our au pair for a year, although so close in age was she to us that it didn't feel like it. She felt more like a friend and was virtually fluent in English from the start. I had just turned 14 and Sam 15 when Christa came into our household. Jake was 8 at the time. We hung out with Christa and later her boyfriend Robin too whose shaggy Afghan coat I coveted (except that it stank in the rain and reminded me of the old sheep experience). They both had long chestnut hair, Christa's shiny and straight and Robin's curly and wild. One Saturday night they introduced Sam and me to The Troubadour club in Kensington. Downstairs in the sweaty, cramped coffee bar we were audience to the various performers, poets and emerging songwriters who I envied, not just for their undeniable and genuine talent, but far more for the temperament and confidence to do something with it.

Christa was a lovely, responsive person to be around - warm easy company that required little effort. We smoked together, talked politics into the night, her brother's involvement as a student organiser and activist* and music, of course. Always music. Her presence made a noticeable difference. It was a rare and much valued win/win situation: our parents could entirely approve of someone who us kids connected to so naturally and easily.

Everyone, without exception, thought highly of Christa. According to my father she was the 'right kind of German person'. This sounds highly politically incorrect now but it mattered at that time. Christa being young, intelligent, politically involved and primarily left wing was in a different class altogether. She belonged to a new informed non-avoidant generation. A generation, it seemed, unwilling to go unconscious to its nation's recent past. This was particularly important to my father.

My father struggled with the existence of 'Germany', or rather to be specific, with Germans of a certain age - the age possibly of Christa's parents' generation. German's who were alive and thriving yet who may have been 'complicit'. He would refuse to drive through Germany or set foot on its soil on our many forays into Europe. The avoidance of the geographical hulk that is Germany posed something of a problem getting to certain places. If we were travelling overnight on a train that passed through its borders, as long as he didn't have to 'see it' or consciously acknowledge its existence, that was somehow just about acceptable. Under the cover of darkness and sleep he could convince himself it never happened. The following morning on the train my mother would whisper things to us such as "We did actually pass through Germany for a few minutes but whatever you do, don't tell Dad". It isn't so strange really considering there were branches of our family who had been wholly annihilated in concentration camps during the war. My parents themselves, living in South Africa throughout the 1940's were fortunately protected from the immediate effects of the war but there were aunts, uncles and cousins in Europe who were not.

To my parent's great credit they had later gladly emigrated from SA (where they had been living a pretty comfortable life) at the height of apartheid and were vehemently and actively left wing and anti-racist. This caused a major and irreconcilable split with the values of their own parents and their generation. I found it incomprehensible, perverse even, that a Jewish person whose own family members had perished in Nazi Europe, whose antecedents prior to that had suffered racial persecution from time immemorial, could themselves in any way, shape or form, hold racist views of any kind. Yet this was the case. The grandparents had maids, servants and gardeners as did the entire white population of SA, but they treated them as undeniably inferior to the white man and were unwilling, it appeared, to have their world view challenged. I could not reconcile this anomaly in my own mind. It bewildered me, it made me ashamed to be white like them and of course, to be a Jew. It maddened and infuriated me but no where near as much as it infuriated my father. In this instance his rage was justifiably felt and had a legitimate target:

One particular incident stays with me and is indelibly etched into the memory banks. It concerned my grandfather, Aaron, and a confrontation that happened at a family passover dinner in London just after the front door had been opened to let Elijah in (as you do). I'm not entirely sure what Elijah brought in with him that night, but the evening and its conversation culminated in my father rising in a fury from his chair and spitting at his father-in-law: "Quite frankly Aaron I wouldn't give a fuck if my daughter married a black man. It would matter only that he were a decent human being". Yes, he had a point and he was making it in no uncertain terms. Though I felt for my shocked and confused grandfather who got it in the neck from dad but just didn't 'get it' at all. How could he?

Sam & I go to Hamburg

Where Are We Now?

The summer after I turn 15 Sam and I are invited to Hamburg. Christa has finished her year in England and has extended the hand of friendship to me and Sam. We're going to meet up with Christa, her activist brother Rainer and his girlfriend and hang out together in Hamburg for 2 weeks.

We're pretty excited. We get the boat overnight from Harwich to Hamburg. I am a little exhausted after a sleepless night on board keeping the seasickness and apprehension under control. This is new territory physically and socially. Christa, Rainer and his girlfriend meet us at the dock. We introduce ourselves and Rainer already looks bored and twitchy at the prospect of 2 adolescents tagging along with them for the next couple of weeks. Who can blame him? He is rather tall and aloof. His gaze drifts to loftier things somewhere over there in the distance. His sleek girlfriend can barely bring herself to make eye contact. I notice she has super-slim ankles because we find ourselves somehow always walking several paces behind them. This is not quite what we were expecting and a different thing altogether from the warm and open connection we've had with Christa herself this last year at home in London.

I admittedly have a simplistic and romantic image of Hamburg possibly from articles I've read in the Melody Maker about the Beatles in the early 1960's cutting their teeth in its clubs and venues. I have the black and white photographs of Astrid Kirchherr in my mind and create my own sanitised version of the city. I want know to where the Beatles once played and what that was all about. I'd like to check out venues such as the Kaiserkeller and the Star-Club. Do they still exist? I haven't seriously done the research. In my naïvety I don't register that these places are likely to be in the seedier, more criminally active parts of town, and probably got closed down years ago. I never get to find out.

We drive through the wide avenues. There seems to be a lot of open urban space I'm thinking before realising that this is probably because large chunks of the city were flattened in air raids and have yet to be rebuilt. I'm surprised at the size of the roads and do my best to banish the occasional military image (tanks, troops etc) that creeps in under the radar. Meat seems to be frying in small stalls on every street corner. All this bratwurst sausage and fried onion - the overwhelming smell is in the air, everywhere. Sausage for breakfast, lunch and dinner. Sam is a vegetarian (though it won't last long, and I'm very soon going to become one).

We settle into the large apartment that Christa has rented. It has a cool bohemian vibe about it: Tall shuttered windows, white painted floorboards and kelims; with rubbery Monstera plants that haven't gone dry and crispy with neglect like the ones at home; there are low corduroy sofas to slump into and the walls are clad in pale ochre hessian just like the stuff you see in the Habitat catalogue. We listen to the free-form improvisations of Amon Duul on Christa's record player and drink litres of Jasmine tea. (Christa tells me all the furniture has been acquired literally from the street: that periodically the residents of each area put out anything they no longer want, the designated day this will happen is advertised in the local press and whoever shows up can take what they need.)

It's hot. Not just hot like in a normal summer, but bakingly, suffocatingly hot. Who knew Hamburg got this bloody hot? In the bedroom Sam and I are to share we are introduced to the 'duvet'. I have never seen a duvet before. It looks enormous and completely the wrong kind of bedding material for the summer though it has an exotic fascination too. I suspect the duvet could smother me to breathless death in this heat with its billowing excessive weight.

It's now about 2 in the afternoon and I think we've run out of things to do and say. It's our first day in Hamburg and we probably wish it was our last. I collapse onto the gigantic duvet to catch up with some sleep and basically, kill time.

Christa and Rainer have a few ideas to keep us amused and specifically out of Rainer's hair. We go to see Andy Warhol's latest film "Flesh" the next evening. I'm thinking 'great, something to do that doesn't involve making conversation with people who aren't remotely interested'. Flesh, though, has been dubbed from English into German. There's a well built naked man in this movie. The rest passes me by since I don't understand a word of it, nor can I make any meaning of the 'plot' but being something to do with Andy Warhol chances are there isn't one. The high point of the evening is the ice cream I'm eating like a good little girl. I feel about 5 years old and excluded from this alien adult world. We go home to the suffocating duvet.

The following day a trip has been planned to meet up with friends 'out of town'. Rainer has procured some super strength black Afghani for us to smoke, which we do before setting off in the late afternoon in his Volkswagen. I have no idea what's in the stuff we smoke but the journey seems interminable. I feel as if I've been captive in this car for weeks. The countryside in the early evening is dark and forested and quite mysterious. I start imagining that we are being kidnapped and any moment now 'the plan' is going to be revealed to us and the ransom money demanded.

Rainer drives like a total maniac, swerving round impossible hairpin bends, almost landing us up in the lake that we are circumnavigating. Is he just a lousy driver or extremely angry? I cling onto my seat and dig my nails into the upholstery. I wonder what would be worse - kidnap or car crash? I'd like to stay alive as long as possible so the kidnap option begins to sound quite appealing.

We arrive at a large gothic looking house in the woodland by the edge of the lake and are greeted by a smiling, seemingly friendly couple and half a dozen or so friends of the family. Thank god Sam is here too. In my paranoid disconnected state I cannot keep the fantasies under control. Who are all these people and what are they doing here in this magic, dangerous forest? Are they talking about us? What's going to happen next? We sit down to eat round an oval oak banqueting table. Is the food normal? It tastes just fantastic, mouthwateringly delicious, but has it been spiked with something? Everything and everyone becomes menacing.

It gets worse. After dinner we are ushered down to the lake for a midnight swim. But it's not just a normal swim. It's skinny dipping. No one has a bathing costume. There's not a chance in hell that I will be doing that. It's bad enough being a self conscious introverted teenager with all my clothes *on*. I watch these athletic, self assured people skipping and tripping down to the water's edge. I hear the echoing splash and splash of naked people messing around in the moonlit waters of this enchanted, treacherous lake. They are free and sophisticated and share a language, a way of being in all senses. I cannot ever be a part of this, though if I could be honest with myself for just a moment, I sincerely wish I could. They seem to belong something and to each other. I don't belong to anything yet, not really, but perhaps this is because I'm simply too young. A voice in me calms me down. It tells me that my time will come. That it will be ok. I am not used to the benevolent voice that comes unexpectedly from some remote region of my own psyche. But for now I am way, way out of my depth and I haven't even put a toe in the water.

Sam & I realise when we wake up back in Hamburg the next morning that we have to get out of this place. This will be our fourth day and it's four days too many. That evening Rainer delivers us to the next ferry out of the city. We say our goodbyes to Christa and I feel that familiar empathy and warmth once again, and I believe, probably for the last time.

We arrive back in London after just 5 days away, cutting our trip short by about a week and a half. The rest of the family have taken off for the south of France until the end of the month, so the house is empty and it doesn't really matter that we're back earlier than expected. We can take over cat feeding duties now from the milkman, who leaves food out each day in the shed round the back for our 5 cats.

Sam & I don't need to conduct a post mortem - we both know only too well what a complete and utter disaster the Hamburg fiasco has been. We can pretend to laugh it off but it hurts more than I'd choose to admit and the bitter aftertaste can't be washed away that easily. It feels so great, though, to be back on familiar home ground once again. There's a small amount of grass stashed under Sam's bed so we roll a joint and smoke it with our tea and toast upstairs in the top room. We're just unwinding and about to turn on the TV when we're disturbed suddenly by odd noises and unfamiliar footsteps coming from downstairs.

"Oh shit!" whispers Sam "I think we're being broken into!"

'Fucking hell' I whisper back 'What should we do!' I'm scared stiff and trembling all over.

"Did you remember to lock up downstairs?" Sam says to me.

'No, I thought you'd done that!' We tiptoe onto the dark landing and try to avoid the creaking floorboards. I creep towards the top of the staircase hanging onto Sam's shirt almost too scared to breath, as if the sound of my breathing will give me away.

Then we hear a voice and a bit of crackly radio transmission.

"It's the police, for fucks sake!" whispers Sam.

Sam grabs the remaining bits of dope and the Rizlas and shoves them out of the window onto the roof and we hope and pray they don't smell anything strange.

"Hello. Hi there" Sam calls out, trying the best he can to sound up beat and composed. "Is there anything wrong officer?"

'What are you doing here?' says one of the three police people who have entered via the back door and stomped uninvited through our kitchen. They are now standing in the hall glaring up at us on the stairs above them. It seems a rather odd question to ask us. Isn't this the question we should be asking them?

"Err, we live here" I say in a wobbly feeble voice that is several semi tones higher than normal.

'Do you now? Do you indeed?' snarls one of our boys in blue. 'Really? I find that rather hard to believe.'

I am thinking what the hell is going on here? This is our house, isn't it? It certainly was when we left for Hamburg and as far as I know, it still is. Sam is looking mystified.

'Can you provide us with some evidence pertaining to the fact that you claim you live here?' says another one who kicks open the door to the study. 'We've been alerted by neighbours in the area who tell us this house should be empty until the end of the month. We can have you done for breaking and entering, you know. You squatters, you little fuckers have really got a nerve. You think you can just break into any property you fancy, don't you now!'

They seem to be looking for other 'squatters' as they suspiciously peruse the rooms downstairs whilst keeping an eye on the two of us looking shifty on the stairs. They must sense we have something to hide.

Sam still has his wits about him, whereas mine have frozen into stop motion memory fragments, dominated by one in particular which I cannot banish: the long, gruesome night of interrogation in Canon Row police station.

"Look officer" says Sam, coming down the stairs and hoping that the pungent residue of dope smoke isn't going to waft down with him "Let me show you my passport. Here, have a look." One of them checks out the passport and hands it to his colleagues.

'And what about you?' he says looking at me. I'm thinking - what? What about me? Oh, I get it. He wants to see my passport too. This is crazy. I rummage about in my stuff and eventually produce my passport from the pocket of my jeans jacket. We've barely been home an hour. We haven't even unpacked and now this. He looks at it, he looks at me. He just doesn't want to make this easy. What is it with these people?

Eventually, after drawing it out for as long as they can, they have no choice but to accept that we are who we say we are and that we do, in fact, live here. There's no apology for the intrusion, for the manner of their questioning, for their intimidating presence. And even though we've done nothing wrong (apart from the smoking of a bit of weed which in any case they are unaware of) it feels as if we've transgressed in some wholly unacceptable way. How do they always manage to do that?

"Jeez" says Sam when they've gone, relighting the butt end of the joint and exhaling "How much worse can it get?"
'Dunno' I say gloomily, not sounding terribly confident, 'Can't get much worse now, surely?'

I call my mother in France. "Hi Ma (this is the ironic name given to her by my father in homage to an American TV series, a precursor to the Walton family, but which has somehow stuck) just phoning to say Hi"

She's hears something in my voice. 'Hi Sweetie, is everything ok? You sound....mmm.. sad? Where are you?'

"Oh Mum, it all went a bit pear shaped in Hamburg. Actually, it was a disaster. So boring - absolutely nothing to do and they didn't really want us there - so we came home early and then the police have just been round to the house thinking we were squatters or burglars or something.....they've just gone, thank god." I tail off.

'Oh gosh' she responds empathically 'Must have been a bit of shock then? We asked next door to keep an eye on the place. They must have reported activity going on in the house. Will you be ok? Have you got any money for food and the basics?'

"Just about enough, I think, we can get by 'til you get back." I'd forgotten about money or food. She sounds so lovely - I suddenly miss her like a small wound to the heart. I feel young and fragile. I want to breakdown and weep. Momentarily my thoughts turn to Rainer, his girlfriend, the police and what links them. Then Davide shows up at the end of this list. The common denominator is that they have no interest whatsoever in anyone else's experience. No empathy. Not bothered should you be struggling with anything, desolate, in need of help. Getting dramatic, I think, they couldn't care less whether you live or die. They really couldn't give a damn.

'D'you want to have a word with dad?' My mother asks, but right now it's her voice I need to hear more than any other. In the background I can hear voices and live music - must be the village fete.

"Just tell him we're fine, Ma. That I miss him" I'm sniffing and repressing the tears.

"Me and Sam are knackered from the boat and then the police and everything. Been a hell of a day. Going to watch telly for a bit.....try and forget about things, you know."

'Ok Sweetie - phone tomorrow if you need anything. Anything at all. Oh and let the milkman know you'll be feeding the cats. Things are bound look up for you soon, you'll see.'

"Thanks Ma, will do. Don't worry about us, we're fine, really. And say hi to Jake from me. He must be bored stiff up there in the middle of nowhere. Bye for now."

Footnote:

Student movement in 1960's Germany

To the students, the German chapter of Fascism was not yet closed. Many former Nazis were still working for the government or at the universities (in fact, then-Chancellor Kurt Georg Kiesinger had formerly been a member of the NSDAP) and the newly-formed right-wing National Democratic Party of Germany (NPD) was attracting more and more voters. In addition to that the students had to deal with the fact that they were identified as Germans and blamed for the crimes committed by their parents' generation.

The students did not want to be held responsible for their parents' deeds. But their parents acted as if it were no concern of theirs; when the students tried to show the public that the anti-fascist idea of the constitution was not yet established in German society, the government and the press felt extremely offended, feeling they had formed a democratic society and did not want it to be attacked - Wikipedia

How the Conrad situation gets resolved

(when I'm 15)

My parents were both clever and pragmatic people (crafty, might be a more apt description). The blue-lined letters at this point, are still landing on the doormat periodically and I've been down to Brighton recently after getting back from Hamburg to catch up with Con. Unable to keep tabs on Conrad's influence from afar (and probably because they are simply curious too) and, since he is temporarily a free man and not actually 'crashing' in Lewes Prison right now, they do an unexpected and possibly rather generous thing.

This is their Masterstroke: They invite him to come and stay with us for the weekend!

I find myself thinking suspiciously and doubting their kind intentions. Is it a case, I wonder, of keeping your friends close and your enemies closer? Surely they cannot be encouraging this dangerous and highly inappropriate friendship? I am now 15 and nevertheless still officially underage and he is a divorced man of nearly 28. Come on?

My mother, with a copy of Elizabeth David open on the worktop, asks me "What kind of food does Conrad like? Is he a vegetarian or will he eat the Canard a l'Orange I'd like to make for you all. I'm thinking of doing the warm chocolate and walnut cake/pudding thing too - the one you have with lots of cream poured into it. Just let me know what you'd prefer. Or, I tell you what, you can have the duck and if it isn't his thing I'll make something extra or separate for Conrad....."

'Whoa! Hold your horses, Mum, please!' Though she's definitely onto something here: I can't imagine Conrad has ever eaten a canard or knows what it is when it isn't floating on water but the very last thing on my mind is food right now.

I'm due to be performing music with a small band of friends this weekend and am wracked with the increasingly familiar and debilitating stage fright. I have an uncontrollable neurosis about everything: what I look like, what I sound like, my liquified brain, I can't remember the words to the simplest of songs that normally I know inside out. I'm truly horrible to be around and steeped in self loathing. Perhaps my parents feel Conrad will be a calming and soothing influence on my jangling nerves and paralysed vocal chords? I must try and be more magnanimous in my thinking, I really must.

Con arrives, and is lulled into a false sense of security by the gigantic blue and yellow flower painted in shiny, drippy enamels on our front door (commissioned by my father, painted by me). For a tiny moment he associates it with his 'people'. Not for long.

As he enters he seems overwhelmed, initially by the size of the house and everything in it (he's never seen so many cats and gerbils! He hasn't actually ever seen a gerbil before) and then by these peculiar chain-smoking people with South African accents. Why are they being so friendly and accommodating? What motive could they possibly have here? Am I about to be busted, again? The father is asking some oddly personal questions but in this super friendly way. What's going on? This is starting to seriously creep me out, it really is! The food smells a bit odd too....

I'm beginning to get flashbacks of my stoned paranoid Hamburg experience just empathising with his body language and darting eye movements.

Conrad spends an awkward and uncomfortable couple of days with us. He is so out on a limb I feel responsible and genuinely upset for him. He has no peer group (too old for the youths and too young for the olds) and virtually nothing here to relate to, except perhaps Sam who is welcoming and open hearted but this only adds to Con's paranoia. So as he and my brother smoke together and watch TV in the top room it does little to ease the building tension. Con's discomfort as I witness it, is stirring up that bleak feeling of not belonging, anywhere.

On the other hand, it's so great to have him here when I have to go on stage. I appreciate his uncritical support when the critic in my own head is ruthlessly picking over every slightly dodgy note I produce. I'm grappling with a mixture of feelings: relief that the gig is over, and dread that performance, after all, is so obviously **not** going to be my thing. And lurking around the edges of my thinking, is a separate and entirely different issue: Where does Conrad fit?

The few private moments he and I grab to hang out together are, I start to realise, a bit uncomfortable all of a sudden; he is stroking my hair, he is saying lovely things; he takes my hand as a gesture of reassurance but now all I want to do is pull away from him. Something feels different. But how did that happen? There's a tangible alteration in the dynamics between us. I can feel it in my body too, just a sense of Conrad's otherness and otherworldliness not seeming quite as alluring or as exciting as it used to. Nothing has changed yet everything is different. I feel a gnawing hollowness in my solar plexus and a lump of recognition in my throat. I try to resist it, with all the energy I can muster, but I recognise the feeling that is rising up in me is something oddly familiar yet strange in its intensity. It is loss. Who are we now? Who are we without these classic identifications? So long as I've cast my parents in the role of the great Oppressors determined to shape my life according to their will, and Con has embodied the quintessential Freedom Fighter determined to release me from their grip, it's all been bumbling along nicely. And more than just that, it's given us a shared sense of mission and adventure - a clearly identifiable cause to rail and rebel against.

These Machiavellian parents of mine have put the kibosh on our raison d'etre and thoroughly undermined our sense of place in the world by being so damn reasonable and accommodating. I feel absolutely ruinously gutted.

How dare they be so bloody nice! Who the hell do they think they are? I am raging.

Yes, who indeed are they? They are Arch Strategists, Skilled Practitioners in the Dark Art of Psychological Manipulation and they have just staged a beautiful, quietly devastating little coup. On the other hand perhaps I am being a bit over dramatic and paranoid and it was simply a lovely gesture on their part to invite my friend to stay? Mmm? I grapple with these conflicting thoughts and suspicions all night long and most of the following week and I still cannot make up my mind. There is only one thing I am sure of..... that I know, without a doubt. *It's over.*

I don't see Conrad again until our paths collide nearly 10 years later.

- - - - - - - - - - - - - -

Hello Kit
Although I don't wholly approve of this form of communication with you, as you must realise by now, I feel I do need to comment on your recent writing for the sake of your own understanding and insight. It is all very well to imagine that your parents had a masterplan. Perhaps this perpetuates the illusion that they were present and available to you, and foremost, aware of the potentially dangerous situation that your 'friendship' with Conrad exposed you to.

I don't want to say much more but I would suggest that you confront your resistance without delay and make that appointment to see me as soon as possible.

Kind regards
Dr Maelstrum

PS and off the record: Your parents are amazing! I wish mine were even half as laid back and open minded.   I   mean   my   mother   was   an absolute.....actually I can't go there. Apologies. Keep up the writing.....

St. Pierre

(Un Petit Village Psychoanalique)

Where Do You Go To My Lovely?

A few years earlier in 1966 my parents who could no longer stand the relentless bone chilling misery of the British climate, decided to buy a place in the south of France. We'd been venturing south each year by car to Italy, Spain, France. Anywhere warm with water to swim in and a stunning view. We are experts when it comes to roof racks, bungies and tarpaulins, which we have to be because the medicine case alone has its own dedicated space taking up half the boot.

The search has been on for the closest approximation to the Cape that they can find within the confines of Europe. Without my father's persistent fear of flying they would surely have chosen to jet off to some more exotic land? However, taking this into consideration they locate the ideal holiday destination in the Mediterranean hills and sparsely populated mountains of Les Alpes Maritime just inland from, and north of Nice and Cannes. Others before them have done the research and the hard graft of getting there, buying and setting up holiday residences. It turns out there's a growing number of psychoanalysts (mainly ex pat SA's currently residing in NW3) who have been snapping up properties in one particular French village, so it is to this village, St.Pierre, that we head in the Spring of 1966.

Perhaps it is a testament to Ezra's love of his work, and Marion's enduring support, that they would choose to take their holidays in a beautiful remote village in the middle of absolutely nowhere, crammed full of his learned colleagues? Is there no getting away from the Freudian contingent, ever? Is there no escape from the feeling of being perpetually observed? Not only are some of these people colleagues but one or two are close rivalrous colleagues, and one in particular is going to challenge my parents on their dubious childrearing ethos.

It turns out it only takes a couple of hundred quid and a few bottles of Scotch to get the apartment buying deal done with the wizened and be whiskered mayor of the village. I'm not quite sure what this transaction actually achieves officially but it ensures we have now have a small place two floors up in a tenement property in the village with a hayloft on the next floor. In return the mayor has left three bottles of the locally produced eau de vie in old fashioned, stoppered, lemonade bottles. This is scary stuff, so scary that even my father in his wilder moments will not touch it for fear of its corrosive properties in relation to his already troubled oesophagus. It remains in the recesses of the cupboard gaining in alcoholic strength for the next couple of decades.

The following summer my parents have the hayloft converted by the artisan builder who has been responsible for the whole conversion. He is the blue-eyed, handsome and charismatic M. Gregoire who happens to live just one floor below us (charisma definitely outweighing building technique, it turns out).

At first he creates a 'staircase' to the upstairs level that is really just a glorified ladder, needing two hands to hang onto it to make it safely to the top floor.

"M. Gregoire!' exclaims my horrified father getting his priorities right "Zoot alors! How on earth will my wife carry a cocktail tray upstairs whilst clinging on for dear life to the rungs of this ladder?"

M. Gregoire obliges by installing 'proper stairs' with a drop that will ensure hospitalisation as there is absolutely nothing to stop you toppling headfirst down the stairwell to the concrete tiled floor below, but at least my mother can now carry the aforementioned cocktail tray upstairs if she is extremely careful. My father is satisfied. We finally have an extra bedroom, upstairs lounge and sun terrace that you can have a party on.

According to Ezra we have the "very best views in the village by miles" which is evidently a big deal if you are South African. But he well may be right. We look out over the mediterranean mountains and slopes with their ancient stone terracing; we stare deep into the valley below us dotted with tiny grazing horses, the skyline is magnificent and at times, threatening with its storms and forked lightening. Most important, as far as we kids are concerned, is that we have a brilliant view of everything going on in the village square.

What we don't have though, is a swimming pool (of course not! We don't even have a back yard!) but the psychoanalyst colleague couple and their kids next door to us do. We hear the laughing and splashing - the soundscape of contented people cooling off and languishing in the dappled, rippling water. We can almost smell the aroma of their newly applied Ambre Solaire suntan lotion drifting up in tantalising breaths to our terrace next door on the breeze. In the heat of the midday sun this suddenly becomes unbearable to my father, who is after all Capetonian and will forever associate warm weather with water to cool off in. I think he might explode with frustration. He skilfully finds ways of getting himself invited next door where he can bask not only in the sun filtered beautiful water of their pool, but also in the company of colleagues who he has plenty to do with back home in London on pretty much a daily basis. They can talk shop to their heart's content. But to be fair he is also willing and highly amusing company.

My mother on the other hand is busy practicing her French in the understocked Alimentation (the sole shop in the village) and supplying Jake with as much of their ice cream as he can swallow to keep his spirits up (he is hot and bothered like the rest of us). My parents also seem to have gone completely over the top with sunblock when it comes to Jake who is covered daily from head to toe in a gelatinous white layer of impenetrable grease, otherwise known as Uvistat.

138

As far as I am concerned ingratiating myself to our neighbours for a swim brings with it the prospect of yet more inquisitive psychoanalysts to contend with, so I avoid. I will sweat it out quietly and grumpily by myself rather than place myself under another pair or two of scrutinising, hypothesising eyes. For much as they might protest, even off duty, even on holiday in these remote mountains, you can feel the clicking and whirring of a diagnosis being clocked up in a shrink's mind a mile off.

There are alternatives to not going swimming next door such as taking a tour around the village doing a bit of shrink spotting from afar - comparing their properties to ours, checking out if we have company our own age lurking somewhere in the form of their kids. Like a miniature version of NW3 there is an imbalance of psychoanalysts per capita in this place (village population 150 ish, peak season psychoanalytical population heading for about 5 or 6 households). If pushed there's always escape to the mountains themselves which, as you watch them, pulsate in the haze with the scent of thyme and lavender and the tinkling of the occasional goat bell breaking through the stifling, claustrophobic midday heat.

However, we do have a secret life in this place too. There are plenty of escapades that happen without the knowledge of any elders usually in the dead of night, such as rally driving/crashing round the mountains with some of the older French kids with near disastrous consequences. There have been minor romances of a teen sort too, surreptitiously playing themselves out after dark in this village and the one across the valley, which have frequently ended in muffled, embarrassing tears and incomprehensible and implausible explanations. And a bit of opportunistic assault in the electricity cupboard under our stairs is, well, not unheard of though not exactly a regular occurrence. Not much child protection going on in this village, it seems.

I will need to clarify the word 'everything' as applied to the statement I made earlier that we can see everything going on in the village square, since superficially nothing much goes on in this village, at least visibly. In this place the arrival of the pizza van once a week is a big event to be anticipated and celebrated. We are a little bored at first and bored senseless by the time we've been coming here for a few years and are well into our mid teens. There are a few things that alleviate it such as the escapades I've described and another of them is getting stoned. This is more complicated than it sounds as we either have to bring our supplies over with us on the car ferry (risky) or acquire it somewhere en route between Calais and the Cote d'Azur (also risky).

Sur le pont d'Avignon (not exactly)

On one of our overnight stops part way through the journey across France this particular summer, Sam, Georgina (whose uncle is an esteemed shrink colleague / author) and I sneak out of the hotel after everyone has turned in and look for somewhere to score. This is more difficult than it may at first appear. We are spending the night in Avignon because the car train has arrived late and we are too travel-weary to complete the last part of our journey tackling the hairpin mountain roads this evening. Sam has suggested we leave the bedroom window open in the hotel as it's on the ground floor to the side of the building and easy to access if we're sneaking in too late to use the front lobby. This makes sense. We are relying on Sam to iron out the finer details of this particular expedition.

Once out on the street we focus our attention on finding people who look as if they smoke and are friendly and benign and more important, unlikely to turn us in to the nearest Gendarmerie. We need to unearth people sufficiently terrified of 'les flique' or at least as terrified as we are. We wander through the avenues just checking out the local youth sitting around in the cafes and bars. There are always telltale signs ie long hair and a certain type of scruffiness. We are seeking out other members of our tribe but it is slightly complicated by none of us having more than a rudimentary knowledge of (colloquial) French. How do you say 'score' en francais? But it matters very little in practice. Sam miming the rolling and smoking of a joint makes it perfectly clear what we're after. My low pass French O level is redundant on this occasion. We find a couple of students who are equally clear that they have what we're looking for.

After an unnecessarily long meandering walk up dozens of side streets and 'conversation' in which all parties are sizing each other up, we arrive at a small sparsely furnished apartment that seems to be in the centre of town. We're offered *un cafe* as we sample the stuff they'd like to sell us. The dope is strong (rather like the coffee) and the colour of the dark earth flecked with white bits (possibly opium?) so probably Nepalese. This is just what we need to take the edge off those boring scorching afternoons when nothing much happens in the village. By the time we've scored (and sampled the product) and are making our way along the shadowy alleyways and *rues* ostensibly back to our hotel we realise we have absolutely no idea where we are. None. It's getting late in this strange town and even in daylight we would struggle to get our bearings.

'Hey Sam' says a giggling Georgina 'It'll be so ridiculous climbing in the window when we get back. I can just imagine it now, all arse over tit! Let's ask the next person we bang into for *les directions*. *"Excusay mwoir avay vu lay directionez? Ha, ha...."* What did you say our hotel is called?'

Silence from Sam who looks at me gesticulating as if I'm supposed to know.

"Haven't a clue. Let me think...... I wonder where we are in relation to the bridge?" I say unhelpfully, and then "I thought you were the one with the amazing memory. You must at least remember the street name, Sam, surely? You *always* remember that kind of thing!"

'How come *I'm* supposed to know that? You complete idiots!' snipes Sam who has neglected his responsibilities as the eldest amongst us. We are in serious trouble.

'Why is it always me who's supposed to know everything?' he snarls in bitter exasperation.

Georgina and I look at each other and we don't need to say it aloud. What we are collectively thinking is *because you always do know everything, always have, always will and you are the brains around here'*. Sam has forgotten that long ago he fought for and attained top spot in the pecking order and now the very least he can do is graciously follow through.

It is a surreal experience wandering nowhere in particular looking for some kind of recognisable landmark in the process of finding an anonymous hotel situated, well, nowhere in particular. It is not that we have forgotten what it is called, we just never bothered to find out in the first place. I barely remember what town we're in. We attempt to re trace our steps. "Didn't we walk past this little park with the boules pit?" says Georgina whose visual recall is still just about functioning.

'No, no way. Never seen it before in my life' I find myself admitting 'Sorry'.

"This is the bench that idiot bloke ran along shouting something obscene about the police" remembers Sam a while later reflecting on our journey to the dealers' place. And it does seem to be vaguely recognisable. "He was so fucking stupid, such an exhibitionist and just asking to be busted.... at least we've avoided that, so far."

Yes, so far, but he wouldn't be the only idiot in these parts I tell myself harshly. My thoughts get considerably gloomier and I imagine having to shamefully hand myself over to the local Gendarmerie at dawn pleading for directions to somewhere that we have no memory of. Three lost (and stupid) stoned *enfants*. It

sounds so pathetic and its beginning to feel that way. I imagine too the parents waking to find us missing without trace. Simply vanished into the night in this foreign city. For a moment I can't even remember which city - is it Avignon or Aix or Arles or.........
Aachen (no that one's in a different country, I think?)

We stop to rest for a while in a small square by an annoying trickling fountain, which only reminds me how much my bladder is aching to relieve itself. I'm desperate in more ways than one and not used to the diuretic effects of such strong coffee nor the way this dope is accentuating each and every physical sensation. Although it is summer, the night has brought a distinct chill to these streets that we have failed to anticipate. Our flimsy warm weather clothes are hopelessly inappropriate. Sensate memory is so unreliable: when its hot it is virtually impossible to imagine the onset of coolness again and vice versa. Georgina has her head in her hands and is rocking neurotically back and forth making the rickety bench we're sitting on creak and sway. Sam on the other hand, is utterly motionless clearly assessing the situation. I am practicing isometric exercises of the perineum, strengthening the relevant muscles. I'm in a cold, clammy, fear-ridden sweat.

To say the relationships between us three are strained would be a gross understatement as we are now barely bothering to communicate at all. In the silence I conduct an internal search for someone or something to blame. I cannot find a target other than myself and the inner voices are getting louder in their condemnation of my own stupidity. It doesn't help that we are all deeply under the influence of the highly potent Nepalese.

Everything is exaggerated. At another time, in another situation we might be congratulating ourselves on our successful appropriation of some shit hot 'shit'. But not now. We get going roaming the streets in increasing desperation. No one seems to have been taught orienteering at school. I don't even know what orienteering is but it sounds like something we could do with right now.

I've never known a night to go and on so relentlessly. A number of times we find ourselves simply walking in circles, returning yet again to the same familiar dead ends, then begrudgingly acknowledging that we have indeed been here before (and not in a previous life).

Just as the sun begins to rise, in our despondency as we wearily turn yet another faceless corner this time there is a vague flicker of recognition as far as Sam is concerned.

"I know we're close" he says getting very slightly excited because he is too tired and pissed off to be any more enthusiastic.

"I just know it. Isn't that where we bought the baguette when we arrived here last night?"

I can now hear my normally self contained brother becoming increasingly animated about bread. As far as I'm concerned this looks drearily like every other street we've so far explored and I can't bear to get my hopes up. The boulangerie across the road is lit up, its log-fuelled ovens anticipating the early morning croissant rush, and yes, on reflection maybe it could in fact, as Sam suggests, be the one we visited last night. At last, I inwardly concede, a recognisable point of reference. Just a few doors down, in fact almost next door, we spot our nameless nemesis of a hotel sitting there innocuously. *How dare it.* It knows not what hateful torment it has caused.

Yet at the same time, the sight of it feels like the destination at the end of a lengthy arduous pilgrimage. Or a home coming at the end of the Hero's Journey (no, make that the Fool's Journey, like in the Tarot deck). But the utter joyous relief. *Once we were lost and now we are found* (or to be more accurate 'it' has been found) we would sing out loud if it wasn't quite so early in the morning. The three of us tiptoe cautiously towards the window we've left open, perhaps our single wise decision in retrospect, and clamber one by one into the bedroom we're sharing where Jake is still asleep, snoring quietly beneath his ruffled bed linen. Oblivious.

At breakfast my mother asks if we've all slept well.

'Oh yeah, really well Ma' lies Sam looking pale and twitchy. 'Had some strange dreams though about getting lost in this labyrinthine wilderness and walking for miles and miles because a pair of dangerous lunatics had forgotten to bother to find out where we were supposed to be going.' He is glaring in the direction of Georgina and myself.

'Are you sure you're ok, Sweetie' says Marion 'You sound irritable and look a little under the weather? And you!' she says turning to me 'Your eyes are all red and bloodshot!'

"Oh you know Mum" I mumble and lie "The allergies in this

place are just awful. I think it's all those avenues of err…. lime trees. Everywhere you look. And I'm not supposed to have feather pillows! My eyes are so horribly itchy, I've been rubbing them all night and now I look like crap, don't I?"

'You're always so worried about what you look like!' she says stating the obvious but falling for the ruse 'I'll have to dig the Predsol* out of the medicine case after breakfast - that'll help with the itchiness'.

"Yes!" My father is now having a go "This obsession with your appearance is getting a bit much, honestly. Especially, this fantasy that you have about your thighs!" he bellows so everyone in the dining room can hear. "And on the theme of this thigh thing!" he adds with broad Capetonian accent, in the midst of creating a new tongue twister "I trust you've talked it through thoroughly with your therapist? Maybe you need to go more often - up your sessions from two to three a week. We'll have to have a proper think about this when we get home, won't we?"

Georgina is hiding her face beneath a large straw hat and behind a big, hefty novel - a classic of some sort. She's unlikely to be disturbed by questioning from either of our impressed parents since she appears to be engrossed in a 'proper' book which bestows upon her an invisible shield of immunity. She isn't allergic to anything (apart from the nature of the conversation and bees) so she can't depend on the itchy eye get out clause. Her own eyes, when revealed a bit later, are much redder than mine or Sam's.

After breakfast as we pull away heading for the mountains

and St. Pierre I now notice the slightly faded and run-down hotel which must have once seen better more prosperous days, has of course been ironically and cynically named 'Xanadu'. This I shall not forget in a hurry, ever.

Footnote:

* Predsol: These drops should not be used to treat a red eye that has not been diagnosed by a doctor, as inappropriate use can cause blindness.

The birth and death of a cloud

Hey you! Get off of my cloud...

Once ensconced in the mountains after our hair raising dope acquisition experience we take full advantage of its potency. A couple of days into our stay I notice there is a cloud that seems to consistently sit all by itself in the otherwise clear sky above one of the mountain ridges. Lonely as this cloud may be it is a mystery to us that it is always there each day in exactly the same position. Is it the same one or are there a series of them? This surely needs thorough scientific investigation.

We set up a row seats on the terrace upstairs and create our own mini outdoor cinerama with popcorn, Coca Cola and a hefty amount of the crispy and crunchy cocktail type foodstuffs Georgina has appropriated from the store cupboard downstairs, normally reserved for 'proper entertaining'. Jake joins us and Sam rolls a fat joint and we sit back gazing at the sky, watching the genesis of the cloud as it forms out of nothing as almost invisible wispy vapours converge and become a little more solid. And then the freshly formed cloud floats happily for a while along the mountain ridge before it magically evaporates and finally completely disappears. And just as the cloud dissolves into nothingness the formation begins all over again. There is something sweet and a little beautiful about this quiet elegant dance of emergence and disappearance happening almost unnoticed in the sky before us.

'We'd never have known if we hadn't bothered to watch - I mean, that it's actually hundreds of newly formed clouds, not just the same one...' I say falling in love a bit with the living and dying cloud. 'How simple and well, beautiful....'

I'm not sure if it's the dope speaking or if something else in me is getting all stirred up. The short mysterious cycle of cloud life, death and rebirth is making an impression either way.

Thus we while away the days in a protective haze until.....

Trouble...

A few days before we're due to leave the village Sam, Georgina and I need to do something with the excess shit hot shit we've acquired and we do not want to risk taking it home through customs. We could either find someone who might want it or alternatively find somewhere to stash it until our next visit. The psychoanalyst family with the enviable swimming pool have an American au pair with them who has already had a couple of smokes with Sam. So he approaches her about whether she'd like to have it (or more accurately, buy the remaining lump from us if possible since it cost a fortune in pocket money in the first place). This is not such a wise move on our part. Although happy - delighted even, to smoke it for free when the opportunity lands in her lap she certainly doesn't want to pay for it, is obviously offended by the suggestion and consequently does something fairly unhelpful. She reports back to her employers that we've been attempting to sell her naughty illegal substances (true) - that we are in fact drug 'pushers' (a slight exaggeration). Her employers in this case are of course, the psychoanalytical colleagues. An almighty row ensues where one of them accuses our parents of raising their kids to be low life dope dealing rubbish, unaware of course, that his own kids are indulging in similar habits and activities, except being a few years older their consumption level is greater and considerably more varied. The whole village can hear what is going on even if they don't understand a word of it.

The row doesn't end that day in St. Pierre. It flares up back home in London intermittently at dinner parties and other social and professional get togethers and will not be put to rest. It is far easier to point the finger at other peoples' wayward children than to look a little more closely at one's own. I don't know if Ezra tries to make this point because he has a great deal of respect and affection for this man's kids and would not want to be the cause of unnecessary trouble for them. The professional relationship I imagine must have been soured because the conflict between my father and his esteemed colleague doesn't seem to resolve itself.

I can't recall being chastised for our misdemeanour and it may well have been due to Ezra being in a prolonged 'good phase' where not a lot shocked or bothered him, his sense of fair play and justice solidly in place.

In St. Pierre where nothing much ever happened this incident lived on gaining mythical status. A few summers before, Sam and I had displayed our recklessness to all and sundry by jumping into the fountain in the village square during one of the annual drunken fetes. The kind of normal thing you do as kids. We now had a different reputation to uphold and nothing could shift it, not even the passing of time and our own maturity. We (that is, the kids in our family and anyone remotely associated with us) became inescapably labelled Those English Dope Dealers from that day onwards and pretty much forever more.

We did eventually find a solution to the problem of the excess Nepalese hashish which involved burying it in a neighbours garden in a small silver box and it getting mistaken for some valuable family heirloom. But that is another story......

A close encounter of a spiritual kind courtesy of the Maeght Fondation

My father in his wisdom had made it a habit to take us all round art galleries where ever we found ourselves on our travels in Europe. When I was very young I used to put up with this appointment with 'culture' without engaging in it consciously. I would drag my feet reluctantly around which ever art museum/gallery we were perusing, and bored stiff I would await the time when I'd get my reward in the form of a fancy double scoop ice cream or bottle of Orangina with a bendy straw. When I got a little older I started to get actively interested. And one gallery in particular became important.

About 45 minutes away from St. Pierre and down the winding mountain roads towards Nice is a perched village called St. Paul de Vence. On the hilly outskirts of this now annoyingly commercialised artists' village, in a pine forest over looking the Mediterranean sits the sublime Fondation Maeght. A hundred and one different qualities single this gallery out from all the rest, but aside from these obvious attributes there is something more.

The gallery, conceived and created by Aime and Marquerite Maeght, was born out of the loss of their son in 1953. Their idea for a gallery came into being whilst in the USA with the artist Leger shortly afterwards. A Catalan architect called Josep Lluis Serp who had already built a studio in Majorca for Miro, was entrusted with the design and construction.

That 'it ' and 'we' came into existence around the same time (ie in the early 1950's in the case of Sam and myself) gives the whole experience an added relevance even though it might be a bit of synchronistic fabrication on my part. It really doesn't matter that much. The fact is we're all in love with the place.

The walls of the gardens as you enter are covered in what look like Miro mosaics but they're not. In fact they were created by an entirely different artist called Pierre Tal-Coat. Spaced out across the lawn there are Picassos and Barbara Hepworth sculptures intermingling with tall pines that lead up to the entrance. Around you, coming in from all directions, is the echoey backdrop cacophony of crickets and cicadas. The place is literally buzzing.

Once inside you can see through the glass walled lobby into a sun filled courtyard created especially for the dozen or so Giacometti bronze sculptures - drippy and oozing, elongated vertical giants and stretched out horizontal felines creating unusual shadows on the curvy terracotta tiles.

Ezra encouraged my appreciation of the Giacometti cat figures that he particularly loved. On one visit he said *'Have you ever seen anything so essentially* **feline**, *yet so incredibly distorted and bizarre all at the same time?'* mimicking the stroking of a skinny cat stretched out before him, no doubt imagining how he could somehow smuggle it out of the gallery unnoticed.

By the back wall of the sculpture courtyard is a small pool – the designated wishing well - where people ritually chuck coins and bored kids fish them out in handfuls and run off with pockets full of stolen change to buy their *glace* at the cafe. That is, before their parents can catch them in the act.

Almost hidden to one side is a Miro ceramic fountain in the shape of a face that spouts water into yet another rectangular pond with more Miro abstractions on the bottom. And then you get to a series of stepped terraces lined with pine needles overlooking the forest – there's nothing at all here but trees and shadows and art works: Picasso's forked wrought iron sculpture figures rising high up out of the vegetation and giant Miro sci fi beings carved out of enormous pieces of marble. Meanwhile, the thousands of crickets and cicadas, imitating a primordial hum in the background, create a kind of busy, trance-like stillness.

Turning towards the main building Chagall's ceramic, painted tiles cover one of the external walls, and we haven't even looked around inside yet. Who cares if we never get to look inside? The beauty is in the bricks and mortar, the gardens and terraces.

But I keep returning to the courtyard. I immediately fell for the Giacometti sculptures when I first stumbled upon them at the age of 12. I didn't find out for years, until one day I came across an old b & w photo, that Giacometti looked very much like my father. Not just his facial features but the perpetual cigarette in his mouth and his whole demeanour. The way his face droops, his drawn, baggy eyes, a kind of familiar humour etched into and out of the facial lines mirroring the lines in Giacometti's pencil /ink drawings. The artist himself died the year we first went to visit the Maeght. It all feels relevant, yet I've never worked out entirely why.

The need to make these connections concrete is a bit of a red herring I guess and it doesn't account for the deep abiding attraction. Put simply, the place seduces you into a particular state of being. And you can feel it. It rarely loses your interest or focus, even after decades of exposure to it.

Then stumbling back down through the almost vertical pine forest that sits above the village, just below and beyond you, in your line of sight, is the curve of the Mediterranean.

Within the parameters of our atheistic upbringing, qualitatively this is about the closest my adolescent self gets to a spiritual encounter of sorts, courtesy of my parents. Whether it has the same impact on them I do not know, though Ezra, looks unusually at peace whenever he is at the Maeght. As far as I am concerned nothing else comes remotely near it. Thus we pay our respects and regular homage to the gods and goddesses of aesthetic form here in this small, unlikely paradise. Whatever else might be going on, right now, it doesn't seem to matter.

Dr Beaufort

If you should ever see her she will remember, **you** *believed her*
And she'll wonder where on earth the time has flown

Back home in London I'd started to see Dr B. It felt as if I'd been
stuck at 15 forever, whilst the stylus on the record player kept
getting stuck on '*I Won't Leave My Wooden Wife for you, Sugar*'
(from The Rock Machine Turns You On which was fast becoming
my favourite underground album of all time, though I hadn't
clocked yet that the song itself was about underage adulterous
sex). So much had happened in the space of a couple of years, yet
I longed, craved more than ever to be older and more
independent and most definitely, no longer underage. There was
nothing Dr B could do to magically speed up the passing of time,
though seeing him made a difference in other ways:

Dr B lived just up the road en route to the West Heath. I'd
wander up there on Wednesday afternoons, barefoot in the
summer if it wasn't raining and occasionally with my guitar. I'm
not sure that Dr B and I shared the same musical tastes or

aversion to footwear, but I did feel for once that he was 'on my side' and less an ally to my parents.

I wasn't entirely sure why I was there, why I had been 'sent' this time. I suspected it was something to do with a general 'failure to thrive' across the board but I cannot remember ever being given a context that I could make sense of.

Dr B's 'style' if you can call it that, was more relational and conversational than I was used to.

It had nothing to do with his appearance which was pretty conventional - pale, balding and in common parlance, 'straight' looking. But I wasn't expecting his easy presence, his unthreatening manner. I genuinely liked him and I could almost allow myself to believe he might like me too. If I had evoked his disapproval he certainly kept that to himself. He didn't pathologise the 'patient' or child in the manner of my other shrinks or as I had often experienced my father doing when he couldn't resist casually offering up an interpretation or two across the dinner table.

Dr B was in fact, the first of my 3 shrinks to suggest overtly (ie not just by subtle allusion)that some of my problems might have had something to do with what was going on with the parents. Why, one may wonder, is the obvious so extraordinarily elusive? He would make interventions such as "Perhaps this says more about your father than it does about you?" or "How does your mother feel about (*your father being in such a bloody sorry state and impossible to be around* - not quite his words, but close)...?" The inference being that perhaps not everything that was going wrong with me was entirely and solely 'my fault' or of my making. I felt reassured by this idea. Not that I, in my more reflective moments, wanted to mercilessly apportion blame solely in the direction of my father or my mother (although being an adolescent it was sometimes hard to resist that notion). I just wanted to make sense of what was happening in the messy universe in which we were living and breathing. It helped to hear that sometimes when people got 'depressed' they expressed it by being angry. That the anger was about them being unhappy and not necessarily about you or anyone else being fundamentally or innately 'bad' or unlovable.

I had begun recently to witness Dad in various stages of meltdown - and though I didn't yet know about his relationship with alcohol he had always been prone to extreme mood swings in the bi polar sense. Even without the alcoholic ingredient those moods were unpredictable and all pervading when he was on a downer. Sometimes he would lovingly tell us kids how beautiful, intelligent and delightful he found us, and he really meant it. He was supportive and extremely tolerant and I loved him all the more for those qualities. At other times he would rage and roar how selfish and disappointing we now were and even, non-specifically, that ' **we had failed'**. We neither knew who he was at any given moment, nor for that matter, who we were and the nature of our apparent 'failings'. That we were loved much of the time was evident, but it was what went on in the gaps in between that evoked the growing self doubt.

And watching my mother handle 'the situation' in that

familiar self effacing way as if she believed she didn't deserve anything better wasn't great. Marion was a confusing role model in that she had so much about her to admire, yet at the same time, no sense personally of what was genuinely admirable about her. She did what she felt she had to and there was a powerlessness about it. An inevitability. I felt it too. And I felt somehow responsible in an irrational way for all sorts of things that I had no power whatsoever to influence.

To Dr B's credit he listened and commented but never took on the role of critical parent. He didn't push the transferential relationship or get too over excited by the idea of 're enactment'. It would have been absolutely the last thing I needed. I never got around to talking about the body dysmorphic 'thigh thing' (as instructed by my father) though indirectly there were many references to the lack of esteem behind it.

   We broached the subject of my getting arrested in Trafalgar Square, even though it felt quite risky revealing it. Talking it through inevitably conjured up Abby's shocked face and the unsettling memories of the aborted therapy with her. Dr B knew, however, that the underlying problem here was the enduring sense of betrayal - the unexpectedly conservative reaction of my parents - and the shaming associated with that night in the police cell that still felt raw. And naturally exploring the sensitive (and possibly sensational) subject of Conrad and the age difference felt similarly risky, though technically it was recognised by both Dr B and me that no law was actually being broken by anyone.

These were the content driven subjects we mulled over, though more important and pressing were the existential ones: I couldn't see the point in making an effort in all the places I was expected to when it all came to nothing in the end. Not much had shifted internally where questions of mortality and therefore life 'purpose' remained unresolved. I was riddled with anxiety and hypochondriasis - and could not easily see beyond it. I did not trust my own body because the body itself, whichever way you looked at it, was so vulnerable and unreliable. In relation to matters of the body, I said nothing to Dr B about what had happened on the ship. I never gave that episode a name such as 'sexual assault'. It was as if everything that had taken place that night had sunk to the bottom of the sea, well beyond consciousness recognition and recall, where it would remain undisturbed for decades to come. Yet despite the helpful conversation with Dr B, in the outer world I would fear the pavement exploding and swallowing me up as I walked along it. In my world there was nothing to stop the earth just falling off its axis and out of the sky. I was screwed up and mightily insecure and masterful when it came to the art of displacement.

Lovely as he was, Dr B didn't have any answers to offer me but then I didn't expect him to. He wasn't a philosopher or a spiritual teacher, he was just a damn shrink after all! Fallible and flawed like all the rest of us, trying to make the best of a pretty mean cosmic joke.

On the subject of trust though, it was a big deal learning to open up to him and to personally acknowledge the benefits of the so-called 'relationship': to feel safe, to feel treated like a person and not just another text book case. It is no small feat winning the trust of a rebellious and insecure adolescent who has every reason to doubt the supposed benefits of the analytical process. This formed the central theme of our work.

There were complications that I did not recognise overtly at the time but certainly sensed implicitly: Dr B belonged to the community of shrinks of which my father was a member, along with his nemesis - the analyst who had made the drug dealing accusations in France. In fact Dr B had co-authored books with the aforementioned psychoanalyst although at the time I did not know this. I found myself torn between longing to tell 'it' as it was, 'it' being the complexities of my family life, my own raw feelings, and simultaneously finding myself ferociously protective of my parents, my father in particular. It felt like a massive leap of faith to trust that what I revealed would go no further than the four walls of Dr. B's consulting room, yet I could not fully entrust that this was the case and in all honesty did not believe it to be so. I found myself saying more than I perhaps intended, which intensified the feelings of betrayal. So the spit between betraying or protecting those to whom I was most attached inevitably intensified over time.

Perhaps what finally won me over, and shifted the balance, was that Dr B had the good sense to use language and conversation that I could relate to and avoided weird 'therapy speak', thereby creating a sense of distance between him and the shrink club vernacular I was familiar with. For example, he didn't go for maddening and alienating interventions such as 'what are your masturbation fantasies?' or 'I can imagine you have sadistic/hostile feelings'. And he never once left me hanging in the swallowed back silence that I dreaded. (That ridiculous, purposeless silence that so many shrinks genuinely consider to be an effective analytical 'tool'. Whereas, particularly with kids and younger people, it is far more likely to be experienced as an alienating and distancing device.)

By the time I left therapy I could openly credit Dr B for having 'made a difference'. I was willing to acknowledge that this time, 'the help' may have actually helped and I was just a little sad (or perhaps even more than a little sad) at the end of our final session, the following spring, when we said goodbye.

- - - - - - - - - - - - - - -

Hello Kit
Thank you for this last 'instalment'. It has been an interesting and enlightening process hearing about your therapeutic relationship with Dr B. He seems to have done some solid work with you at a time when you were receptive and open to being in therapy. A brief window of opportunity, if you like. It is heartening to hear that you were able to feel met and valued by this particular psychoanalyst. What is it that impedes your receptivity to the work now? I would appreciate a response from you at your earliest convenience.

Regards, Dr Maelstrum

PS Dr B? Who is this guy?

Hi Dr M

Might I sense a shift in tone coming from you? Have I written something that has offended you by any chance? I hope not.

Best,
Kit

Better Safe...

One morning before school my father starts to make conversation with me in the bathroom. He is taking a stock check of the items in medicine cabinet before making his choice for the day ahead. Rattling the bottles and taking off his glasses to double check the labels and contents, he completes the inspection.

'Must get some more Valium' he mumbles to himself 'And we seem to be a bit low on the Mandrax too...hmmm...that's odd? ' I say nothing.

He then informs me 'By the way, Mum and I thought you should go and see Rosalie (gynaecologist) and get fitted up with a diaphram. You know, a contraceptive cap?'

"Yes Dad! I do actually know what a contraceptive cap, I mean a diaphram, is."

'I know you're only 15' he says all casual and upbeat 'but better safe than sorry and it's good to be prepared, isn't it?'

He smiles and grabs a handful of pills and trundles out of the bathroom humming.

"Okey dokey" I respond and inwardly rejoice. My liberal parents have definitely been handed back to us by the Bodysnatchers.

School's Out & Estelle

She Talks To Rainbows

During the last couple of terms at school I'd formed a friendship with a girl who'd just joined the 6th form called Estelle. It didn't require much more than a momentary glance to recognise a kindred spirit and ally. But there was something deeper. She was all gung ho on the outside and shaky as hell on the inside, rather like me.

The school had recently abandoned its dark bottle green uniform. There were all sorts of sensible justifications put forward for this though the real reason was glaringly obvious: The 'girls' had found a way of making the uniform fashionable and sexy. The sight of hoards of skimpily attired, kohl eyed, chain smoking schoolgirls was way too much for the governors to handle. Our school skirt had to be bottle green, other than that there was no reason why it could not be worn as short as possible and be made to look more cool with the addition of long black leather boots and black fishnet tights. The look was pushed to the limit by the midriff revealing cut off shetland jumpers that had just caught on. The whole concoction made us appear not dissimilar to the sexualised St. Trinian 6th formers depicted in the films. Collectively we were attracting an awkward amount of male attention at the school gate. In desperation the apoplectic governors got rid of it realising they could never control the 'modifications' that were being made, preferring almost anything including ancient dishevelled, ripped up jeans, to this provocative bastardisation of the once beloved school uniform.

Thus Estelle arrived aubergine-hennaed and in full exotic gypsy attire announcing to the world in no uncertain terms to which tribe she aspired. She had escaped oddly from a progressive school which she loathed in Hertfordshire. (I could never quite get my head around this - since it sounded great to me but then I didn't have to endure it as she did.) Estelle's Indian dirndl skirt was embellished with a gigantic burn hole, courtesy of a fiery lump of cannabis resin that had recently landed in her lap. She jangled as she moved and exuded enough patchouli oil to overpower the nausea inducing chemical smell of school on the first day of term. Estelle started to hang around at our house whenever she could, where her skirt acquired a few more burn marks to balance up the original gigantic one. Her parents were somewhat dubious about her association with our unconventional household, particularly her father who imagined he could still exert some influence over his daughter's unstoppable gravitation towards the 'alternative'. His daughter, didn't he realise, was way beyond rehabilitation. A respected physician, her father and mine came from opposing philosophical camps, the one exception being their shared deification of 'Academia'.

In different ways Estelle and I were both outsiders looking for somewhere to belong. I felt increasingly alienated from my contemporaries, such as Helena, who were focussing successfully on getting A levels, applying to university and seeing the point in it all. Apart from the small matter of it being well beyond my capabilities, university held no appeal. Estelle had struggled to fit in at her former school and struggled once again to integrate herself into this elitist north London grammar school. Belonging was the big unspoken issue: To what, to whom, to which causes and passions? And seriously, what really mattered anyway?

This was the era of tuning in, turning on and dropping out if you lived in San Francisco. The era of living communally on a windswept rural island in a village of tents and teepees if you were brave enough. School inevitably came to represent the stultifying, stuffiness of convention and yesteryear. School represented conformity and dreariness and impending wage slavery. Out there in the wider world there were small pockets of something highly intoxicating bursting with a brand new energy and vision. It was massively attractive, at least, that is what it looked like from the other side of the fence. Culturally, we were both drawn to the underground scene, to progressive music, to the arts, and primarily to saying 'no' to conventional expectation in whatever form it presented itself.

The search for approval of and inclusion into a new alternative and mythological 'family' grew more tantalising. Estelle and I indulged ourselves in a fantasy that involved us absconding with the charismatic male members of The Incredible String Band and living out a utopian lyrical existence in a dreamlike fairy woodland with their lot and a bunch of gentle milk yielding goats (or whatever). My hair by now was wildly, reddish-blondly pre-raphaelite and waist-length and in my mind's eye visually I could slot myself easily into that alternative rural idyll no problem (that is, if I airbrushed out the long list of allergies to pollinating and itchy, furry things).

At weekends I hung out with Estelle in and around Portobello Road where we scored our weed in the local Wimpy bar. Pembridge Villas became the key destination for the Victoriana we acquired for the wardrobe: embroidered silk shawls and ancient shenille curtains that had been turned into floor length skirts; the occasional 1940's crepe tea dresses sometimes made an appearance. My favourite item of clothing was a fitted, pale turquoise velveteen coat that swept the ground. I think it might have been a chic dressing gown of sorts in a previous incarnation and I could imagine it belonging on a 1950's Pinewood film set. I wore it with my mother's long black skirt, the one I had stolen, which she didn't much care for anyway.

Both Estelle and I shared a naïvety and idealism in the extreme as we envisioned ourselves appropriately clad in this alternative highly seductive reality. It was just about the only thing that could counter the existential morbidity that dominated my thinking, and the similarly troubling images that dominated Estelle's. Something had to give and soon.

It was no secret to anyone that I had been planning and envisioning my own great escape from the day I had arrived at this school but the denouement itself falling a few months short of my 17th birthday turned out to be a little anti climactic and low key. Semi consciously I had begun to spread a rumour that I was leaving (wishful thinking perhaps and certainly my intention) and the rumour took hold as rumours do.

I'd signed up to take a bizarre set of A levels such as British Constitution and Ancient Greek, in a half hearted attempt to slough off my past failings in more mainstream subjects and start afresh. I could never remotely imagine staying the course (along with the other daydreamers and distracteds taking these subjects). A little later that term my British Constitution teacher, Mrs Elkin, not expecting to see me in her diminishing class, said in surprise "Oh I thought you'd left a while ago?" Her statement gave me the green light. I walked out then and there minus my parents' knowledge or consent and never looked back. There was not a molecule in my body or being that regretted the day I left school and no doubt my frustrated teachers were as blessedly relieved as I was.

It was early March in 1971. My parents were beside themselves. I found a way to appease them and buy myself some time by enrolling with Estelle to go to a local FE college to do A levels in the autumn of that year when the new academic year would begin. The thought of all those months of freedom from March until the end of September was unimaginably liberating and sweet. I could not believe my good fortune. I had been hanging on in there at this school and it felt like forever, but Estelle, my new partner in crime, had lasted less than 2 terms. I knew exactly what her parents were thinking and what they felt about my somewhat 'unhelpful influence' even though they seemed not to register that she had dropped out quite some time before I eventually did. But we were both, selfishly perhaps or in the name of self preservation, well beyond caring at this point. I was nearly 17 and I didn't want to waste another precious moment of my life on irrelevant and utterly meaningless activities.

Part Two

_____

Crash

November 1971

Ok....shhh... I'm whispering because it's the middle of the night and I'm in Lawn Road Hospital. Next year, they say, this place is going to become the state of the art Royal Free Hospital, but right now it's a run down dilapidated wreck awaiting demolition.

I'm here perched on the very edge of my bed. There's absolutely no way I can imagine sleeping. I can't even touch the skin on my arm it hurts so much and my hand right now is resting on this pillow because it seems to feel a bit better like that. I don't think my arm is honestly the main problem. They won't give me any pain relief because I'm a 'head injury case' so they've put me 'under observation'. I'm fairly used to being under observation but not this sort. I've been down to the X ray department in the basement and then back up to the ward and had stitches in my forehead just above my left eyebrow. At least it's stopped bleeding now. I personally think I was a head injury case long before I ended up in here, but now it's official. I've been pleading with the nurses to come and relieve my agony with some kind of medication. Give me morphine for god's sake! Look at this lovely vein! But they won't or they can't. Oh, I haven't said why I'm here....

I've been knocked down by a car. I don't know where to start. I've really messed things up.

It's been a seriously wild, stormy November night. I can still hear it pissing it down outside this hospital window. I sort of have an image, more like being in a dream sequence, of rushing down the hill, Briardale Gardens, to get to the bus stop. The rain whipping relentlessly at my skin, slithery leaves all over the pavement - water soaking through these stupid non-waterproofed suede boots. Water getting absolutely everywhere in fact: into my eyes, all mixed up with my hair and the distorted blurry streetlights and my crying too, I guess. I was in a desperate panic state, that much I do know. I'd been trying to get to see Marc. But now I hardly remember what that was about. Let me think......

Oh yes. I wish I didn't remember but it's all coming back now - just such a searingly nasty feeling, worse even than my bloody arm or my bashed up head. Like my heart is sinking through the soles of my feet. It's all gone so badly wrong and there's fuck all I can do about it. *(I'll get back to what lead up to this happening in a bit when I can bring myself to talk about it....... but not right now, if you don't mind.)*

I remember just as I dashed across the road to catch the bus, spotting this car out of the corner of my eye, trundling almost towards me. The irony. I got run down by a pale blue Morris Minor. Christ!!! If you have to get run over does it have to be by a Morris Minor for god's sake? How mundane is that? I can't exactly write a song about my tragic, life-threatening encounter with a Morris Minor, can I? Like a Monty Python sketch or worse still, a tawdry country and western ballad. It's really true what they say though. Time slows right down. It's amazing. The theory supposedly is it gives you time to think and act in an emergency, hopefully. And also what they say is that there's no fear in the moment. I do clearly recall the thought that passed through my mind as I saw the car coming towards me and there was absolutely nothing I could do. I just thought *'Oh, well'*. No fear whatsoever. How about that?

And then I do have a vague picture of this distraught wide-eyed woman getting out of that car. Middle aged and grey wiry haired. She looked terrified. Like she'd seen a ghost. I must have said I was ok. Because somehow I got home on my own. Oh shit - I transgressed mightily tonight. Oh no..... it's just astonishing how it's coming back to me but it's exactly like remembering a dream or a maybe a film. I charged into the house through my father's waiting room with blood all over my face and clothes, wailing and sobbing, with this guy close behind me, hot on my heals. The patient! She was just sitting minding her own business in the waiting room when this nutter (me) comes crashing through her world. She must have thought I was being accosted by the guy.

How would she have known he was trying to help me? That's it, I vaguely remember him being at the bus stop. He must have seen what happened and followed me home. Then in my screwed up, disoriented state I can see myself upstairs in my room a little later feeling out the gash in my head and it was horrific. Fingers full of sticky, coagulating blood and pulverised flesh.

Next thing we're in the car going to hospital and I'm holding a dishcloth up to my head to stop the bleeding. My dear father is saying ' **_You're going straight back into analysis, my girl_**! ' Jeez his timing is terrible! He sounds so damn angry and he's smoking furiously, taking it all out on the cigarette he's sucking the life out of. At least he's driving me to hospital first to get stitched up. Why is it that analysis is more important than fixing my actual real physical head wound? Then he's muttering something nonsensical about *unconscious suicide attempts.* What on earth is he banging on about? His latest theory or what? The last thing I want to do is kill myself, doesn't he realise? In fact, I'm obsessed with staying alive forever - hasn't he been listening all these years? But obviously he's decided that's what I'm trying to do - top myself, apparently. Just like he decided years ago that I was trying to deliberately impale my finger on a razor blade. The old self-harm theory. Is there any point telling him where to get off? I'll shut up for now and keep swabbing at my forehead with the dishcloth, if you don't mind.

Where's my mother? She must have been there. But why don't I remember her? We're in the X ray department now and they're X raying different parts of me, especially my head and neck. I have whiplash (obviously). I have the head injury where my head hit the ground. So I have to have stitches. Something is very wrong with my arm because it shouldn't be this painful, but it isn't showing up. I must have tried to break my fall with my hands because a lot of skin has been scraped off my palms and now there's a nurse bandaging them up. That's about all I can recall of the last few hours.

* * * * * * * * * * * *

Ok. Thank God, I got through the night, just about. I think the doctors must have realised that they missed something. I've been sent back to X ray this morning and the radiographer has spotted a fracture to the scaphoid bone; it's now set with plaster and is marginally less agonising. Still no painkillers though. They say I have to stay here a few days so they can keep on eye on me.

Sam & Marc are coming to visit me later and Mum too after work. Oh and I haven't told you about Marc which is how this all started.

Marc

A Change Is Gonna Come

I cannot truthfully say Marc was my first 'real' boyfriend, because apart from Conrad who was never exactly in that category, there were one or two others and a particular 'someone' who meant something. That someone was the first person I slept with. Alex came from a wealthy north London Jewish family and was in my estimation, pretty damn cool. We'd met at a party and I was impressed with his tallness, his crazy afro hair and maroon velvet flares and the fact that he was an accomplished musician and guitarist with his own band - quite something for such a young guy. We were around the same age and shared similar underground musical tastes, and though I would never in a million years admit it, perhaps culturally in the ancestral sense too, we shared common ground. I liked him and felt safe in his company and he seemed to like me.

When we decided it was time to lose our virginity we planned it, sensibly, and carried out the act with military precision in an almost technical, considered way avoiding any possibility of pregnancy. We waited for my parents to take themselves off for the relevant weekend and made sure I was at a safe point in my cycle. (I couldn't bring myself to use the aforementioned diaphram.) I found it fairly scary but Alex was responsive and considerate, something I had not yet learned to value and appreciate nearly enough. After that I began to lose interest, and maybe he did too and we drifted apart, sort of.....

I carry a great deal of shame in relation to Alex when I allow myself to go there. It's not that he was the proverbial 'one that got away' more that he treated me with decency and respect and had I not been so peer influenced and weak willed, it might have had 'legs' so to speak. I'm not entirely sure what I was consciously looking for in a guy but Alex seemed not to have 'it' at that time. What Alex lacked was the streetwise machismo that seemed to be disproportionately important to me - he wasn't independent enough or old enough to be devastatingly attractive in that sense, but then neither was I. Obviously it is pretty much impossible to be independent at the tender age of 15 or 16 and we both struggled with that unavoidable fact and awaited our much longed for 'freedom'. I tended to gravitate towards an edginess or rawness (as evident in my attraction to Conrad) when it came to my romantic interests, which I often mistook for a philosophical stance or lifestyle choice.

Unbeknownst to me until much later in my life, the driving force or attraction eventually revealed itself as a deep dark wounding to which I was magnetically drawn which had nothing whatsoever to do with freedom, non conformism or alternative living. And the other thing was, Alex wasn't Gypsy enough.

One of my close female friends at the time who had attached herself to a cool, alternative bunch of people, was particularly mocking when it came to my involvement with Alex - her comments culminating in something staggeringly superficial to do with a tee shirt he was wearing that didn't quite fit with the culture. Her comments seemed to demean and belittle him and I was fool enough to fall for it. Or maybe to be fair, her words compounded my own misplaced doubts. Within the blink of an eye, as soon as we had parted, she made her move on him. I discovered an uncomfortable truth in that act of sisterly betrayal that would repeat itself later with other female 'friends' I believed to be trustworthy:

Never trust someone who is hellbent on persuading you to separate from your boyfriend no matter how concerned they **appear** *to be for your well being. And, never forget to uncover what their own personal motivation might be.*

Thus Alex and I went our own separate ways and I could not help but wonder, from time to time, and particularly in my lonelier moments, what might have been.

There is something perhaps symmetrical or fated in my meeting with Marc, as the female friend who made her move on Alex was by then involved with Marc. They clearly were not a match made in either heaven or on earth, in fact their connection had turned out to be rather antagonistic and sour, so when she introduced us it came with a bit of a warning from her: "He's not that considerate actually, so watch out!"

Marc was 24 and I was nearly 17 and just out of school when we got together in the Spring of '71.

Those years that separated us felt huge to me as Marc had done his time at college, qualified as an engineer before spectacularly dropping out and had then actually *'gone on the road'*. Yes, as in Helena's purist definition of it. When we met he had recently returned from some long experimental months travelling around Europe. He had eventually found his way onto the Greek islands where all sorts of mind expanding occurrences had been making their impact on his brain, whilst concurrently an intoxicating dose of sun, sex and sand had, it seemed, been making an impact on his body. I was truly and utterly in awe. And besides having a glamorous and beguiling CV he possessed a head of thick dark hair, parted in the middle, that reached below his shoulders and a beard of biblical proportions. (I thought quietly to myself that he looked the spitting image of the caucasian Jesuses in those pictures you see hanging on the walls of religious households.) Around his neck Marc wore a strand of dark blue glass beads entwined in strips of plaited leather that he had acquired in Crete which went with the blue greenness of his eyes. He clearly did not belong in this world and I desperately wanted to belong with him in whatever world he might have sprung forth from.

I was overcome with shyness and self consciousness in his presence and inevitably made endless stupid remarks whenever I opened my mouth. Nothing flowed. One day up in his West Hampstead attic bedsit listening to music I lazily referred to Monteverdi's madrigals as 'opera' (I guess I mean't to say 'classical' singing as opposed to 'popular' singing) and that he found shockingly unacceptable. I felt I had humiliated myself and revealed that I was in fact, deeply ignorant. I could tell that assumptions to do with my family background had a way of masking my personal lack of education and sophistication in the eyes of others, who expected and presumed I knew far more than I did. Although occasionally temped I continued to avoid reading, I wasn't cultured and the ongoing state of emergency playing itself out in my emotional world didn't leave much space for learning and information retention. Marc had yet to discover this gigantic, gaping flaw in my personality. Often I suspected he saw what he chose to see and I would experience a sense of him barely knowing at all who I was. What I did discover though, was my highly attuned capacity for adaptation and tolerance. I could be whoever he (or anyone) wanted me to be. A lover, a workmate, a mother, a child, a friend, a playmate, a housekeeper, an echo, his shadow. I had become expert at fitting myself around a situation, any situation, and anticipating whatever was required.

Marc was a sensitive and knowledgeable guitarist and this I found an overwhelmingly attractive and admirable quality. If I composed the songs (which had become an increasingly important and stabilising process to me) he then arranged them with a subtle lead guitar that took them musically to another level altogether. I wished he had had some vocal prowess too so we could have created harmonies to my melodic lines but he didn't feel he could offer this. He wanted to improve his classical guitar technique, so this he would do deep into the night, grappling with Ferdinand Sor and complex Bach sonatas. I was fascinated by that particular singled-minded focus of his that was alien to me. He did things 'properly' whether it was memorising a piece of music, designing and stitching together a leather bag (which he was doing on commission) or discussing The Glass Bead Game or Count Keyserlings Travels with his mates. I on the other hand, busked it or bluffed my way in the world most of the time. I started to notice the differences more than the similarities. The unspoken voice in my head would remind me that 'I had it easy' whereas Marc, the eldest kid coming from a single parent family and fraught stepfamily scenario, had had to fight for every advancement he had made by force of his own tenacious will and self belief. His lovely mother, when we met, was holed up with three of her 5 children in a dingy, one room bedsit awaiting council rehousing having been mightily shafted by her latest lover. He'd somehow got hold of the deeds to her property and now she was homeless. I empathised inwardly with her plight, thinking, feeling, fatally recognising that it could so easily have been me with my proclivity for a certain kind of guy.

The first time I brought Marc home was on my 17th birthday. My mother had prepared a celebration lunch starring the reliable Canard a l'Orange, that sumptuous feast of duck plus exotic accoutrements redolent of something straight out of a gastronomic photo shoot. But the gnawing tension and awkward silence that came between us all stole away my appetite and I was so painfully nervous I couldn't lift the fork to my mouth without trembling. I saw my father shifting uncomfortably across the table, no longer his interested, ever-enquiring self, my mother doing her best to lift the tense mood with her divine offerings and my brothers nowhere to be seen the minute they could escape the table. Marc's arrival disturbed us all to the roots and marked the very end of my childhood. I had brought my lover home and my father would have to contend with this other adult male presence now in our lives.

Nothing was ever straight forward in the world of love and romance in my limited experience. Marc had been wildly attracted to a distant contemporary of mine around the time we met. I knew her vaguely from the circle of Hampsteadites I'd hung about with circa the 'gatherings' era. He did not hide his interest in her from me and I quietly, despondently wished she would miraculously evaporate, get kidnapped by aliens or snapped up by another boyfriend asap which in fact turned out to be the case, the boyfriend that is. I often wondered what would have happened had he not shown up in the nick of time and whisked her away. It set up a persistent loop of self doubt that reminded me I wasn't really 'chosen' and convinced me that I was most certainly second choice at best. It didn't do much for the shaky self esteem and kept me somewhat on the back foot in this new tentatively developing relationship with the enigmatic Marc.

I was just at that point of wondering how the hell I was going to hold Marc's interest for a moment longer when out of the blue, he gives notice on his West Hampstead bedsit and suggests we go and live in Wales together for the summer.

Summer of '71

(Wales, Glastonbury, Wales)

Going Up Country...

I am stunned! Don't know whether it's a *'wow'* sort of feeling or a *'whoa! hold on a minute'* sort of feeling. We are packing Marc's Saab with our tatty belongings and heading off towards the Brecon Beacons and river Usk. We have sleeping bags, guitars, blankets, books (not mine of course) some of Marc's leather patchwork bags that he might sell or 'exchange', a gigantic box of groceries courtesy of my anxious mother (who clearly doesn't know they have food in Wales too) and a tent (just in case). I don't exactly have my parents' blessing but I'm guessing they realise there's little they can do to stop me going. And besides, Marc appears to be a responsible, pragmatic adult so no doubt they recognise I'm in good capable hands.

It's all very exciting and nerve wracking - we're driving through the night and intending to get to Wales in the early hours. Something's been on my mind though. Recently we went to see an astrologer. I'd never done anything like that before. Her name was Anne Severson, a quietly spoken American living in the plusher end of Notting Hill Gate. I waited in her fancy, flower festooned living room whilst she saw Marc first. When it was my turn I sat by her white grand piano, faded lily petals collapsing onto its shiny surface, whilst she fiddled with the ephemeris and mapped my chart. The first thing she needed to establish was my exact time of birth because I was on the cusp between two signs. So I went in thinking I was a plodding, heavy earth sign and came out having been informed that I was in fact, a dynamic fire sign, with a fire ascendent and a dark and troublesome scorpionic moon (no kidding, who would have guessed?)

Identity crisis is an understatement? I am allegedly a ram so why do I feel more like a sheep? It's made me question whether the 'real me' is still in hiding somewhere yet to be discovered and dare I think it, enjoyed? Something else she said has been bothering me. She told Marc he would have 6 children. Yes. Six. She told me I would probably have 2. I now feel even less secure about our relationship because there's certainly no way I'm going to be having 6 kids with Marc or anyone. But then maybe it's all bullshit anyway? What the hell. Why am I winding myself up like this when we're just setting off on this brand spanking new adventure?

Now we've arrived the 'situation' isn't nearly as clear cut as I thought it would be. We're staying by a canal in Tal-y-bont with Marc's friend Ivor. Ivor is one of those mavericks: bearded, white haired, of an unspecified age - a complete non-conformist with a penchant for unusually patterned, chunky jumpers, who has built his own canal side home with his bare hands, just about. He has a great wife (fun, but probably compliant and utterly dominated by him) and what seems like dozens of kids. They run a family business to do with boating.

I can tell immediately that Ivor is fine with us staying a day or two but he has no intention of putting us up (or putting up with us) for the whole of the summer. I feel awkward and lacking in relational skills. I don't know where to put myself. I start to help out in the kitchen rather than become the dead weight in the room that I fear I will, sucking up oxygen and contributing nothing to the conversation, which at any rate seems to be all about planning permission (or lack of it) and tedious technicalities. Marc doesn't seem to carry the same neurosis or sense of being irrelevant that is so central a feature of my own feeling state.

Within a day or so we are living with Ivor's friends Jo & Jason who have a little daughter, Rosa, who has just turned 2. They live just outside a nearby village called Bwlch, which is unpronounceable to a non Welsh speaker, but sounds like the way you might feel after a night of excessively heavy drinking. It isn't pretty.

Jo & Jase's remote cottage is a mysterious mix of modern and ancient. It appears contemporary and architecturally designed from the outside - all plain clean white walls and sharp angles. Yet beneath its outer structure it is in fact about 250 years old. It's as if they've covered the ancient cottage in modern cladding but once inside our part of it - the attic - therein lies an accumulation of hundreds of years of dust. It is truly ancient and dilapidated and I believe haunted. At least that is what Jo & Jason seem to be insinuating with their ghost stories and florid renditions of tales of unsolved mysterious deaths that have apparently taken place along these spooky lanes, and perhaps still do.

Marc and the wife, 'thin-lipped Jo' is what Marc calls her, clearly do not get along. One day getting fed up with his non-meat eating habits she throws a large frozen fish at him at dinner time. *'Here go cook that!'* she shrieks and storms out of the room grabbing Rosa by the arm practically dislocating her shoulder. The husband, Jase, a pacifier, dashes after her whilst trying to make a joke of it to us. I identify with him. Marc and Jo are obviously running both of the shows here and Jase and I are the ones who mop up after the spats and disagreements. Who could blame Jo? She has a young kid and a laid back, easy-going husband and now these two non-contributing urbanites to blight her happy home life. We make an effort to do more round the house and get the shopping in. But I secretly wonder if we are unwelcome cuckoos in their small nest.

Having never lived in the country before I am shocked to discover it is nothing like the pictures on the Incredible String Band album covers. The narrow winding lanes and high hedgerows which are so great to speed down in a convertible are not so great to walk along when that combine harvester or fork lift truck is about to come careering round the very same corner where you just happen to be collecting wild flowers for your dining table at home. The other obvious yet initially ignored problem is the grass pollen allergy. It's not so bad at first - a little sniffling, itching and wheezing. Nothing out of the ordinary that cannot be remedied by the killer antihistamines that I have with me. After a day or two though I cannot lie on my back in bed because all I do is cough. Marc cannot sleep because my incessant coughing and hacking is keeping him awake and he is in a foul, vicious temper. I discover I can in fact stop the coughing if I sleep bolt upright in that old mildewy armchair which may in fact be the origin of some of my allergies, being undoubtedly the source of a million or so dust mites and mould spores. In my weary dishevelled way I start to feel just like Anthony Perkin's mother propped up in the chair in Psycho. I am dead to the world, with swollen nasal passages so stuffed up they might as well be filled with concrete and I'm beginning to get a bit freaked out by the wheezing sound coming from my chest. I long for dull days and heavy rain storms because the pollen count will then go down, and I loathe all these beautiful, breezy summer days because all they bring is physical misery. No one told me it would be like this. I am becoming perverse and twisted and secretly I want to go home.

I consult my mother, the Doctor. 'Hi Ma, my hay fever is fucking awful. It's just the pits! The pills aren't working. What am I supposed to do with myself? Please?'

She suggests hot steamy baths and plenty of non feather pillows to prop my head up at night. Oh yes, and a visit to the sea.

She says it will definitely get much better around unpollenated sea air. I have no idea where the sea might be in this land locked hellhole of a place. Marc doesn't really want to go to the seaside but that isn't the point, is it? It's not about buckets and spades and sticks of rock, I try to tell him, but he doesn't get it.

Jo & Jason's spooky tales continue and I begin to wonder why they might feel the need to scare us half to death with stories of the grizzly occult happenings in this 'ere part of the world? And why do they do this so late into the night when we're most susceptible? I find myself afraid to be upstairs in the attic after dark. My ears become attuned to each and every tiny little noise I perceive and invisible beings seem to be scrabbling across our tiles in the dead of night. I sit up wide awake in the Psycho mother chair, tracking these sounds all night long until the light eventually arrives and it feels safe enough at last to surrender to a tentative, upright, snuffle-ridden sleep.

Marc decides we need a break from all this unbelievable heaviness - it's really so uncool and what purpose does it serve anyway? Mmm..... I'm beginning to wonder.

Really, if I'm deadly honest.... I feel so broke up I wanna go home.

Glastonbury: June '71

Trippin' on a Hole In Your Paper Heart

We're heading off for Glastonbury - it's the second day of the second year of the midsummer festival at Worthy Farm and they're calling it Glastonbury Fayre this time. It's supposed to have a Mediaeval theme this year. Already as we drive eastwards there are interesting goings on in the sky above us. The clouds are almost writing themselves across the sky - as if they have a message which goes something like "Hey man it really is going to all work out, just you watch!" Or some such utopian nonsense. I feel uncharacteristically upbeat.

The road leading to Worthy Farm is full of latecomers and stragglers like us who drift lazily towards the the heart of the festival site. People carrying tents and rucksacks, some on the road using anything that has wheels, from shopping trolleys and wheelbarrows to ancient converted coaches and farm machinery. All life is converging towards the site. Just over there in that dip is the newly designed pyramid stage. There are thousands here. It feels like a huge leap of discovery. We are in the land of the kindred spirit - people like us with all the trimmings plus some more challenging extra curricula stuff. The hair, the disintegrating denim, the feathers, the flowers, the beads, the music, the free food and weed and the nudity (which makes me mighty uncomfortable and envious of those disinhibited enough to enjoy it). The pyramid stage is state of the art sound technology or something like that but more than that it is based on mystical geometric principles. It has supernatural powers apparently. It shimmers in the midday sun emanating its extraordinary radiance out to all. Or maybe I just made that last part up.

We've found a great place to pitch the tent amongst a copse of shady trees that line the edge of this field. Marc is clearly an expert when it comes to putting up a tent, or rather, he seems to know what he is doing, whereas I'm on a steep learning curve as his green assistant, having never camped in my life - far too physically challenging for me and my kinsfolk. After we've sorted out the domestics we go looking for some chai. It's a strange phenomena that everything is free. Yes, absolutely free. How can they do that, I hear the Inner Pragmatist argue in my head? Dunno, but they can, so shut up and just enjoy it, goes the Free Spirited Optimist from the other side of the cerebral hemisphere. I am started to feel at home here and people are talking about multiple rainbows round the sun and other natural or maybe supernatural occurrences that we missed by not getting here a day or two earlier. Something's been a happenin' here and I'm not sure what it is.

Marc is relaxing in the sun reading Jung's 'Memories, Dreams, Reflections' crosslegged by the tent. He looks absorbed and content, whilst all around people are dancing and chanting in various stages of undress and applied body paint. He tries to engage me in conversation to do with the Jungian ideas and concepts he's recently been getting into. I'm starting to get involved and interested whilst simultaneously getting thoroughly distracted by the beautiful people doing their thing all around us and there's a new band warming up on the stage. I notice something we share in common, Marc & I, we are both introspective and reserved by nature. (Though I think of him substance wise as *slate*: slightly shiny if you buff it up but impossible to see your reflection in it. Impenetrable. Keeps you safe and dry but can crack, split and become brittle. I think of myself in terms of a substance and I am a *sponge*: frayed around the edges, able to mop up everything spilling out around me. Super absorbent. Yes, I'm a sponge.) Yet despite these obvious differences you won't easily see either of us becoming disinhibited without a fair bit of help from various intoxicants and even then it's highly unlikely. We are both contemplative types, I guess you could say, yet temperamentally, as in *slate and sponge*, we are completely and utterly unalike in every other respect. I hold that paradox for a while before the God of Hellfire, Arthur Brown, appears with a massive burning crown on his head and a chicken under his arm and leaps in a psychotic frenzy onto the stage to perform 'Fire'.

For the rest of the lazy afternoon Marc and I meander back and forth from the stage area to the free chai stall where they are handing out Indian barfi, taking in the vibes and the intoxicating incense-infused atmosphere. There are plenty of fabulous people performing, but the music itself is simply a backdrop to the ambiance that is developing around it. I can't work out if we are in a scene from the end of this world or a scene from the beginning of the next one. Are we in 20th Century Britain or in some out of kilter mediaeval era? Or alternatively, are we unwitting participants in some futurist utopian experiment?

Later that night we wander through the tented area stopping off to warm up by one of the camp fires and share a spliff or two and bowls of aloo gobi and less exotic foods like the macaroni cheese out of the tin we're being offered just now with plastic forks. And in response to the openness of the people we encounter I wonder if this is a community that I could belong to, not just at festival time, but for good. A big part of me hopes that it could be so. I start imagining a future that has small holdings with chickens, maybe goats too. I see myself immersed in nature, as if this is the parallel life I *should* be living. I include in this picture an urban element too, an occasional place in the city, Notting Hill maybe, and why not, to balance out the rural living when an injection of culture is needed. Next I can hear and imagine us making communal music in a funky barn and dare I envisage it, I begin to extend the fantasy to a family of my own. All of us, kids included, are dressed up in a mixture of contemporary and mediaeval style clothing. Out of time, out of place, not of this frustrating rigid, scary world at all. We all have spectacularly outlandish hair and headgear. Sort of tribal. We are making something, creating something together, though I'm not entirely sure what it is. In this other world of my own desires and longings I can't tell whether I'm with Marc or with someone else who I have yet to meet. I lose myself utterly in the fantasy whilst around us, echoing through the festival site there are tribal sounds now of drumming and giggling, and then as the night progresses, orgasmic panting and groaning and eventually, snoring. For a short time all is peaceful and just as it should be. No conflict, no worry, no hassle, man.

But as the adrenaline, kicked into action by the newness of the situation, starts to wear off, I begin once again to succumb to the rising pollen. Adrenaline is the enemy of allergies. It's the one thing that I've noticed keeps it naturally at bay. The irony is that as I relax and start to get into what's going on around me I get sicker and sicker, whilst the night air clogs up with a conglomeration of nasty pollinating substances. The very last thing I feel like is orgasmic.

By the next morning I can hardly breathe and Marc's skin tone has turned a whitish green with panic. I can hear someone vaguely recognisable on stage tuning up. But right now I couldn't give a damn about music. Marc leaps into high velocity action, grabs our sleeping bags and rips the tent from its pegs, as I sit gasping for breath on the grass trying to find more of the super strength antihistamines somewhere in the darkest recesses of my overflowing bag. I stuff a double dose into my mouth without bothering to find water and their bitterness sticks in my throat. Marc has to virtually carry me to the car. I don't tell him then but I thank the gods, who ever they may be, that he is so phenomenally practical and together and I love him fiercely, for amongst other things, those earthy qualities.

As I drift in and out of hystamine induced sleep on the homeward journey I remember the conversations Estelle and I have so often had about dropping out and living in the sticks. Or setting up a commune in a forest. That's never going to happen now, no way, how can it? The fantasy world I cooked up last night is fading rapidly. By the time we arrive back at Jo & Jason's horrible haunted house in Bwlch it's around midday and I'm barely conscious courtesy of the drugs that are, at last, taking effect.

Being terribly upset (which involves a fair bit of crying) does little to alleviate the symptoms. I realise there are serious limitations that I will have to learn to contend with. But I am furious with my over sensitive body that reacts so violently with its environment and has an agenda entirely of its own. I wonder if it goes deeper than the obvious medical explanation I've been given countless times. Intuitively I can sense it but I cannot understand it with my rational mind. My body is saying no to something but I don't know what that is or what that is about.

Val from the Valleys

Yes, The River Knows

White-haired Ivor from the house by the canal tells us about a spiritual healer he's heard of operating out of Ebbw Vale. We decide to chance it taking the opportunity to explore the valleys en route. The idea of healing, faith or spiritual or whatever, fills me with fear and dread for some reason. Perhaps it's being brought up by pragmatic, atheistic doctors that has made me this cynical but obviously there is something else in me that must think differently otherwise why would we be making this trip? Closer to the truth might be the simple fact that I'm just plain desperate.

We arrange to meet Valerie the healer. Val sounds strangely familiar on the phone though I can't put my finger on it and I am going to her for help because I don't know what else to do. None of my mother's medical suggestions have done the trick. We drive towards Ebbw Vale through the tiniest winding roads I've ever seen. Everything else looks as if it has been shrunk too. The bunched up terraced houses lining that hillside are minute like something out of a kids' picture book or model village but with a shadowy edge. This is no fun town, it's a hard working industrious place about a million miles from the tourist information office version of Wales and the benign gentility of the region we've been staying in. It's all railways and steelworks and industrial chimneys responsible for belching out god knows what. Finally the succession of breezy pollen-infused summer days gives way to a massive thunderstorm that soaks everything in its path including us. My lungs at last breathe in the fresh, moist air and by the time we arrive drenched on Valerie's doorstep for the healing I'm feeling absolutely fine. I notice she has gnomes in her front garden. I haven't ever met anyone with gnomes before.

'Welcome to Wales' (or rather Way-ells) she says warmly, and I cannot bring myself to tell her we've been here for what feels like an eternity. 'How can I help?'

Val is a small, blond haired woman of about 45 with startling blue eyes that don't let you get away with anything. Those eyes are like secret weapons tracking your every thought and movement.

'Do you know anything about spiritual healing?' she enquires after placing me in a wicker chair in her living room.

"No, not really. Well no, absolutely nothing. Do I have to have faith for it to work?" I ask her somewhat nervously but she can read my thoughts so why am I bothering to say it?

'No dear, not at all, you don't have to have faith.' She says kindly but somewhat firmly. 'You don't need to be a believer. It has *nothing* to do with faith or anything to do with believing, *believe me*.'

I am slightly poleaxed by Val's paradoxical response but get the gist of what she's saying. She looks at me as if she's known me forever and I begin to wonder if we're related. Then she puts her long-fingered hands not exactly on me, but just a few inches from me as if she's touching a protective shield that surrounds my body. I have no idea what's going on but I start to feel very still and rooted. Like a sturdy tree with thick roots into the earth.

'Bit of difficulty breathing then?' she mumbles almost to herself as she moves her hands across my chest and throat.

"Mmm yep" I respond now as if from another planet, though I

haven't enjoyed breathing this much for as long as I can remember. I let myself drift and float as Val does whatever she does.

'Had, what can I say, a rough time of it then?' she murmurs as if reading my body like a map.

"Kinda rough, couldn't breath - panicked a bit" I say but it all feels like a vague and distant memory from eons ago. And it really does. I am so far away from that experience I wonder if I was to open my eyes right now I'd see planet Earth, a small shiny blue and green marbly thing, spinning happily somewhere light years below me.

'Bit of an emotional roller coaster too I think? Isn't it?' She pauses, taking stock and does something else with her hands, like a flicking motion.

'Yes, a rough ride emotionally, isn't that right, dear?' She pronounces a bit later on, bringing me back down to earth. This time all the feelings spring forth from inside and before I can censor them, they emerge in the form of water falling from my eyes down my cheeks and landing in my lap. I say that because this isn't crying in the normal sense, just the release of sheets of water carrying years of bottled up stuff. 'It' all comes gushing out and I've become a human waterfall. At the same time the nature of what 'it' is, is somewhat of a mystery to me.

'Just let it go, dear' she says as if entirely familiar with this response and it's happened a thousand times before 'Let it go, that's it, let it all come out'.

I think of all my exasperated shrinks, even patient, empathic

Dr B, and if they could do what Val has just 'done' whatever that might be, their consulting rooms would be full to bursting (or conversely empty, as everyone would be sorted).

Finally Val rests both her hands on my shoulders and I begin to feel 'joined-up'. All the messy and fragmented parts have converged into a coherent 'whole' (for the time being, anyway).

'I think you'll be fine now' she says matter of factly, giving me one of her laser looks which seems to be saying *I know exactly what's going on with you, my girl* followed by a slightly crooked, verging on naughty smile that releases the tension.

Down the road in the greasy spoon Marc & I mull over what's just happened.

"I dunno if I'm 'cured' because it's a shit awful rainy day out there so maybe my pollen related symptoms would have buggered off anyway" I say, not entirely believing my own words nor entirely signing up to what may have just happened. Staring into the puddle of baked beans on my plate, I do get though, that it's not just about the obvious symptoms.

Marc is curiously silent and contemplative and suggests I see how it goes, which obviously I have no choice but to do. But something is stirring, even if I cannot put my finger on it. And he hasn't touched his beans on toast.

- - - - - - - - - - - - -

Hello Kit

I was in two minds regarding whether to continue this 'correspondence' with you. However, I feel quite relieved to hear that your positive projections onto Dr Beaufort have now been put into perspective by your life changing experiences with Valerie.

Kind regards, Dr Maelstrum

PS At last! Perfect Dr B's fallen off his bloody pedestal. Rejoice.

- - - - - - - - - - - - -

Hi Dr Maelstrum

Maybe you need to *"get a life"* !

Kit

Evangelist of the White Light

There is a Light That Never Goes Out

Jo & Jase have been ratcheting up the intensity with their increasingly spine chilling stories of the supernatural forces at work all around us. According to them the spirits are intent on driving us away, and their latest theory is that my respiratory problems too are actually the work of these evil entities. Of course, they've been attempting to drive us away (or insane) since the very first day of our arrival, but neither Marc nor I have wanted to accept this entirely hostile state of affairs. So the spirits and Jo & Jason have been in cahoots all along then? Surely our peace loving, easy-going ways are a joy for all to be around? How can people (or spirits for that matter) be that uncool and uptight? We are thoroughly perplexed by the meanness and pettiness of Jo & Jason's attitude and wonder what kind of bad karma they might unwittingly be accumulating for themselves and poor little Rosa.

The tension in their cottage eases up as soon as we announce our imminent departure and there is an unspoken truce of sorts. The look of blessed relief upon Jo's face is a wonder for all to behold but it begs the question, has our presence honestly caused such degrees of anguish and torment? Apparently it has, according to Ivor who eventually 'fesses up that our hosts never much wanted us there in the first place. That they never really 'took to us'. Who would have known? Thank you, dear Ivor, what kind of friend are you anyway, one may well wonder? I am deeply unimpressed by Ivor's callous attitude.

Quietly, once I get over feeling so unwanted, I am rather pleased as I've had about as much as I take of the beautiful countryside and have developed a deep homesickness for the stinking, noisy, litter strewn streets of London. My lungs would happily swap country air for the pollutant infused fog of the city any day.

Now we're back in town Marc has reconnected with some of his pals - an American couple called Tom and Caroline who are living in a basement flat at the top of Fitzjohn's Avenue in Hampstead. Tom is so laid back and super relaxed he is almost comatose. He has a natural warmth and openness that puts everyone at ease wherever he shows up, normally. Yes, normally you'll find Tom with his leather cowboy hat pulled halfway over his eyes, a bunch of tangly pale hair floating down his back whilst he picks away at an old bashed up acoustic. Tom comes from a large family of pig farmers in Iowa but I get the feeling Caroline is most likely a sophisticated, highly educated New Yorker. They are chalk and cheese. Being rather in awe of her and shy in her company, I never do get to find out.

Tom however, has suddenly undergone a massive personality transformation. He has almost given up the weed and has become a spiritual evangelist, virtually overnight, it seems. We wonder what on earth happened to the laid back guy we used to know and love? He tells us he has found enlightenment. In fact he talks incessantly about what he refers to as 'the White Light' which is beginning to annoy another of our American friends, Clem, who comes from Detroit and happens to be black. "What about the black light!" protests Clem who is taking all this rather personally and tends to see things from a more political activist viewpoint. Clem, who normally has a humorous disposition not dissimilar to Tom's, now seems perpetually annoyed and wound up. When Tom mentions the whiteness of the light (which he does with increasing frequency), Clem looks as if it's only a matter of time before he raises a clenched fist and responds with the black power salute. Marc observes these unsettling changes in his friends in a rather dispassionate analytical way on the surface, yet inwardly he clearly needs to get to the bottom of Tom's frankly weird personality transformation as a matter of urgency.

Within days of our return to London, ever restless Marc is tracking down the source of the White Light. One evening a week or so later after successfully locating a meditation centre that seems to be admitting responsibility for Tom's transformation,

Marc reports back how he argued all afternoon challenging anyone present on every conceivable aspect of their 'philosophy'. A big part of me is thinking what a load of rubbish they must be spouting, whilst a very much smaller part is wondering if there's anything in it. Marc remains unconvinced, yet it seems he cannot stay away from this place. Is this because of his love of a good, wholesome argument and the prospect of endless metaphysical debating or is something else going on here? Whatever it is, he is compelled to keep going back for more.

The nihilist in me is making a big joke of the whole process but I too cannot keep my thoughts from wondering, what if? There is a debate of sorts going on inside me too that goes something like this.

On the one hand: 'Who am I to be so bloody arrogant as to dismiss this as a load of codswallop when I know nothing about spirituality or issues of consciousness and am after all a mere speck in the greater scheme of things?'

On the other hand: 'What a load of rubbish - give me a break - who are you kidding'

Then: 'But what if there's really something to it? And I am just too frightened/rigid in my thinking/in denial /fill in the blank etc to be more open minded and give it the benefit of the doubt?'

Followed by: 'Nah! Just let it go for god's sake!'

And finally *In the dead of night, insomniac, driven almost mad by the conflicting voices in my head, I sit downstairs in the kitchen with a cup of tea and cigarette:* 'Why can't I stop thinking about this? Why is it troubling me to this extent? And it's not as if I'm so content and together in my own life. I've been looking for something to connect to for as long as I can remember. Take the night terrors, for instance. All that fear of non-being. What if this could make a serious difference in that department? This could be important so why do I want to dismiss it? To to keep trashing it?'

Ad infinitum. Until one night Marc returns to the house and I can tell something has happened. After we go to bed and he thinks I'm asleep he sits bolt upright and seems to be meditating or doing something that involves being very still and quiet. As I notice him silently practicing whatever he has just discovered I also notice my own undeniable envy.

In the morning I quiz him and find out he has indeed been taught how to meditate. How did he go from being so deeply, unflinchingly cynical to this? Something in me finds this unbearably difficult to be with. Considering I'm the one with all the unresolved existential issues, how come *he* is enjoying this state of consciousness, this state of apparent on-going contentment and dare I say it, bliss? Yet I do not fully understand why Marc's initiation into this form of meditation disturbs me to this extent and is even bringing out a mean-spiritedness in my feelings and thoughts. A few days after his revelation, I have one of my own. I admit to myself that I want to learn how to do this as well. Apart from the dictates coming from my own inner voice there's never been anything standing in the way of me doing exactly what Marc has just done. So I put myself out of my misery and go ahead and ask to be initiated.

In the process I find out there's a spiritual master. He's younger than me and I'm only 17. So that makes him, well, incredibly young. And I'm genuinely grateful to him for what he seems to have opened me to because I can sense right from the start that it's going to generate some degree of stability at last. Putting all the pieces together, I remember vaguely hearing that he made an appearance at Glastonbury but it must have been before we arrived.

Upstairs on the 28 bus going home that day, after my first taste of what meditation actually is and feels like, a complete stranger taps me on the shoulder and asks me what I'm on.

'What am I on?" I say in surprise not understanding the question and then I realise he thinks I'm stoned and probably wants to score. We are travelling through Notting Hill after all. The thought makes me smile. Could it really be that I look that at ease with myself and the world or is he trying to pick me up? Seriously?

The one thing I know for sure, without doubt and unquestionably, is that I am beginning to feel a little safer for the first time in my life.

However, neither Marc nor I quite turn into white light evangelists in the manner of Tom, I am relieved to report, though my parents are less than happy and naturally perturbed by this new, unexpected departure from the norm. It sends them way out of their comfort zone.

College

(allegedly)

At the end of September that year Estelle and I honour our promise to our parents and turn up at FE college in Barnet. The parents collectively have reason to fear for our future. Since in the eyes of mine I now also practice some weird Eastern philosophy they believe I am pretty much beyond redemption. It is striking that they don't notice that I'm rather less neurotic in my general behaviour than I used to be. But as we know, you see what you expect to see. For example, I decide to stop eating meat altogether because I cannot square up watching the lambs playing in the Welsh fields with the stark fact that they then show up dead on my dinner plate. My reasoning is simple and goes something like: why should they die to end up on my plate when I could so easily eat something else? My parents are as disturbed by this decision as I am by the dead lamb I'm no longer willing to eat. I'm not sure this indicates that there is necessarily something up with me, but then it all depends on your perspective. And perhaps, I would like to suggest to them, it may indicate that I am developing a conscience. In any case, I'm unlikely to suffer from any major nutritional deficiency, if that's what they're worried about, as I love eating as they well know.

However to get back to the original point, Estelle and I are signed up to study Psychology and Sociology for A levels. I cannot say I'm exactly brim full of enthusiasm at the idea but I'm willing to give it a go. College it turns out, smells exactly the same as school did on the first day of term.

In Psychology we study toothpaste. And then we study cigarettes. There is a logic here. We are studying the ***psychology of the advertising*** behind these products. Let us consider cigarette advertising:

What does ***Woodbine*** conjure up for you? In my mind I see old emphasemic men in the country on their last legs enjoying a fag or two in the sunset. What does ***Peter Stuvesant*** evoke? I see the international jet set coolly inhaling their sophisticated smokes whilst slaloming at tremendous speed down a Cloisters ski slope. Or alternatively, sunbathing in Saint Tropez whilst discussing the Cannes Film Festival in the company of Brigitte Bardot and Roger Vadim. What about ***Rothmans?*** I see posh, self-satisfied businessmen awarding themselves massive bank bonuses from Coutts. Or conversely, maybe a couple of Mods on Vespas hanging out in a coffee bar with the juke box blasting out Small Faces singles. ***Players No. 6:*** I see Estelle and myself digging around for enough loose change to buy a pack of 10 down at the off licence. ***Benson and Hedges:*** I see estate agents selling your lovely house from under your nose even though you never put it on the market with them. It's a great party game: **Lucky Strike**? (Cool 1950's dudes - maybe Sam Moriarty). **Embassy**? (Self explanatory). **Camel**? (Deserts of course, Omar Shariff and Bedouins) **Dunhill**? (Tory councillors guffawing to the lame jokes of a slick after dinner speaker, whilst twiddling their oversized moustaches). Estelle and I could have so much fun with these.

This is our introduction to psychology and it is relatively engaging in that it invites some degree of creativity and freedom of thought. Next we study experiments to do with lab rats and I start to glaze over and shut down.

I don't remember anything of note about sociology and I'm having a bit of trouble feeling motivated and getting to grips with the point of being at college. Then I begin to imagine two years of this. Yes, two whole years. There are so many more relevant things to do other than study lab rats and cigarette advertising, surely? Prompted by the usual sense of urgency: the impending end days and apocalyptic thoughts, I start to get cold feet. *Question is, dare I leave since I've only been here for just over a month? I'm afraid I think I dare. Yes I think I do.*

This time round Estelle stays on a little longer than I do. Oh, and now she also practices some weird Eastern philosophy. Her parents are beside themselves.

What will you do?

Ride a White Swan like the people of the Beltane

The atmosphere at home isn't exactly harmonious. I have committed a cardinal sin. I have offended the great God of Academia and now my fate is resting precariously in the hands of......... well, I'm not sure quite what.

The question **what will you do** is hanging in the air between us, dangling like a corpse. It's in the banter at breakfast, and encoded into the comments made throughout the day. We cannot even watch television without it rearing its insistent head at every given opportunity. The answer I'm afraid is simply **I don't know.** By dinner time I still don't know and by breakfast the next morning I'm none the wiser. I decide the best course of action is to avoid all eye contact and possibility of conversation. I stay out of the house as much as I can and take myself off to Haleans.

Marc has been to Haleans. Many of the people I admire have been to Haleans, therefore there's no reason why I shouldn't go too. Why Haleans? Firstly Haleans' list of employees lends itself to artistic, creative types: not just fine artists, but actors and dramatists, musicians and performers, writers, poets and journalists, also political asylum seekers and the enterprising student supplementing their grant in the holidays. There are a number of less interesting employees on the list but they are generally speaking outnumbered by the sorts I have outlined above. What is Haleans? It is a top notch, well, umm... domestic cleaning agency. How do I know so much about them? My parents have been using their services for years. In fact, one of the highlights of the week would be coming home from school on a Thursday afternoon and chatting up over tea whomever Haleans had sent to clean up our mess. (They always seemed to send us males.) It's only a matter time now before *I* am going to be expected to clean up our mess if I don't get employment pretty damn soon.

At Haleans' office in Swiss Cottage I sit in the cramped waiting area and I don't feel the least bit out of place. I sign up and am amazed at the excruciating low pay. How is anyone meant to live on wages this low? The hourly rate won't even cover a measly pack of No. 6. We are expected to work in 4 hour blocks and had I not been living courtesy of my generous parents I would need to be scrubbing a solid 48 hour week to make ends meet.

However, working for Haleans is an educational experience. How else would one get to see how others live? What better profession to hand you on a plate an opportunity such as this? I now have access to the most intimate details of my client's lives: their habits, their obsessive compulsive disorders, their medication, their varying levels of hygiene and those of all their close relatives, what they eat for breakfast, lunch and dinner, their social lives and the type of partying they engage in and even their sexual activity. What am I supposed to do with that vibrator I find in the middle of the bed I've been asked to make? Do I leave it where I find it or place it discretely in the bedside table draw? Or in the washing machine? Or under the pillow? What is the etiquette I should be applying? No one gives you specific instructions at Haleans so one is forced to make a series of quick fire executive decisions which I'm sure must be character building.

I do meet some extraordinarily interesting people. There's a kind, sympathetic baroness in Hampstead Garden Suburb who takes a liking to me and bestows upon me gifts such as crocheted blankets or wicker baskets each time I leave. She also fills me up with cakes from Louis' Patisserie in my breaks. I feel a bit like Little Red Riding Hood leaving grandma's house laiden with provisions. The owner of the vibrator is a Canadian music director with a large family of red headed kids and a much younger lover. She gives me cheese. Gorgonzola, dolcelatte and various Scandanavian cheeses I've never heard of. Then there are the ones who cannot see you as an equal and treat you, well, like a domestic (which is of course what you are). The elderly mother of one of my Jewish clients looked me up and down one day and asked me if I too was a Jew. When I said yes I am, she declared in dismay '*My dear girl how did you sink so low?*' I don't imagine she was expecting an answer because what can you say? I just nodded in faux horrified agreement and got on with the hoovering. Then there are the households where it is spotlessly clean before you even get the duster out. These are the most frustrating. There's no sense of achievement whatsoever cleaning a house that is already fit for a cleanliness fanatic and that is exactly who the client is. The 4 hour session feels like an eternity. These are the ones I least like.

In between the episodes of domestic servitude I do bits of market research, analysing questionnaires and coding them with Marc. He has found this work through Sam's girlfriend's contacts and I get shipped in periodically to help out when they're short staffed. We invariably end up researching meat. It feels like a conspiracy, since I've only just become a vegetarian, that I now have to code these questionnaires according to the descriptions people have given after sampling ghastly processed meat products. The code frame we formulate from their answers usually goes something like: moist, meaty, juicy, tasty, succulent, tender, stringy, grisly, salty, sinewy, tasteless, bloody, insipid, flaccid, inedible, disgusting. Then there's the 'x' we have to put against anything that doesn't fit within the code list eg a description such as 'nauseating'.

All the while I can sense something else brewing up.

Marc is getting restless. His feet are itchy as hell. He is virtually stamping them in frustration. I can feel it intensifying as the days pass. Any day now he's going to break loose. Break down the stable door. He tells me he wants to go travelling again. In fact, he's always just on the verge of leaving. I want to shout *"What about me*!"* because I don't seem to feature in his plans. I stay silent. I dare not ask him too much because the truth, if it excludes me as it probably does, would be too difficult to face. He gets more absorbed in Jung. He attempts to explain the theories around the anima and animus. Big expressive outpourings about the anima - the archetypal femme fatale in his words - and his inner feminine equivalent and her seductive powers, the capacity to bring a man to his knees (or something way over the top along those lines). It makes me feel ill. I want my presence to have some degree of sensual and emotional impact on him but I know there are very few anima projections coming my way. He is a passionate person but he doesn't demonstrate feeling particularly passionate about me. We are friends, mates even. A part of me is inwardly screaming *'For fucks sake, I'm only 17! It's got to get better than this, surely!"* Then I realise I'm desperate for him to be just a little besotted, to sense that I move him and stir up some excitement in his body and being. But it just doesn't seem to be like that at all. It's all cool and distant and rational. How can that ever constitute a successful happy relationship when the heart of it is suffused with this degree of ambivalence? I try to banish these thoughts with the facts: We've been virtually living together now for months; we get on brilliantly, have loads of shared interests; we're the proverbial 'great team'. It doesn't work, not at all, and I get inescapably that it's only a matter of time before he announces that he is moving on.

One cool Autumn afternoon when we're upstairs in my room at home he begins to talk in a way that I am finding difficult to hear. He's serious, his head is lowered and he looks me in the eye. He hesitates, takes a drag of his roll up, then starts to put words around the doubts I have secretly been having. He states his intention to leave 'at some point' without saying directly that he is intent on breaking up with me. I hear more about the damn travelling, the 'finding of himself'. *But he includes something else about his feelings for me. Though I know what he is going to say I shut down inside.* I block my ears and turn away and go blank. I can see his lips move but I can't make full sense of what they are saying. From the other side of this glass wall I try to speak, to ward off the unpalatable truth. And then suddenly he throws on his jacket and leaves to go and stay at his mother's place 'for a while' as if he's giving me a taste of what is likely to come. I feel absolutely stunned, rejected, ripped apart even though I knew it was coming, I could see it miles off like a tsunami racing across the ocean. I still cannot remember what he actually says, the specific words in those moments, because my mind and thoughts have frozen over in sub zero shock. Adrenaline is surging through my heart at a terrifying rate and I panic. I have to see him to talk it through, to understand, to somehow *make it be different, force it to be so* and it simply cannot wait. I try to hold back and calm myself down but it isn't happening. It's a hell of a wild and windy November night when I eventually grab my coat and leave the house to seek him out.

Back on the Hospital Ward...

I Can't Make You Love Me

Marc and Sam have just visited the ward and left a few minutes ago. It's about 24 hours since the accident now. After all that's happened Marc seems concerned, not angry or annoyed at me like I imagined he might be. I thought he'd be absolutely furious, but he's being sensitive and warm towards me. Sam was pretty balanced - asked all the relevant things about what it feels like to be nearly flattened by a Morris Minor and then made some observations about this ward: I think he's insinuating that secretly this is a psychiatric unit except that all the inmates are wearing a bandage of some sort, so his theory doesn't hold up to scrutiny. Well, not quite, I realise, as I look around at the other casualties populating these beds.

I didn't get myself nearly killed as part of some warped attention-seeking strategy, I sincerely hope Marc knows that. I'm not that deviant. It's a strange feeling, like I've given up the struggle or maybe I just don't have the energy to care if I'm approved of right now by him or anyone else. How amazing to be free of that for just a while. I couldn't care less. I only hope it lasts.

Actually the whole thing's been an enlightening process. For a start, my concept of time is all over the place - the beginnings, middles and ends don't add up and there are big memory lapses. I've been thinking about Dad too. The thing about Dad and his Freudian take on everything is that inevitably I begin not to trust myself at all, and that includes my own intuition and instinct. It is as if he's implying he knows me infinitely better than I could ever hope to know myself, yet that's complete and utter rubbish. The stuff he comes out with! But when I'm feeling insecure that's when it gets worse. Then I question my own motivation and begin to seriously doubt myself - and it scares me right down to my bones. Like the unconscious suicide thing he's tried to lay on me. It's just not helpful at all. I wish he realised.

Something a bit surreal has just happened: one of the younger nurses has handed me a packet of 10 Consulate cigarettes. But when I opened it just now all it contains is 2 very neatly rolled joints. I feel quite moved that she's done this and totally surprised. Does she expect me to light up though on this ward? It's already a breeding ground for respiratory disease in here being so hot and smoky - in fact, everyone is smoking like there's no tomorrow at visiting time but dare I light up a joint, seriously? But more to the point, isn't she worried about her job if she gets rumbled? Better say nope to the dope just now. I'll hide it at the back of the bedside drawer. Think I will wait 'til I'm out of here to smoke it with Sam and Marc.

My mother has just walked in, pale as a sheet.

'Hi Ma' I say trying to sound upbeat and feeling massively relieved to see her.

"How're you doing Sweetie?" she asks me. She's just come off ward round at Great Ormond Street hospital in town where she's a senior registrar. She looks very upright and is carrying her briefcase.

'A bit shit, Ma' I'm saying to her 'but ok.... not in so much pain now at least.' I realise I trust my mother. We may not have the closest physical bond in the world but I trust her completely, implicitly.

'Will I be ok, d'you think? I mean is this head injury thing serious? I mean *seriously* serious?' There is something reassuring about the fact that she is both my mother and a doctor.

"You'll be fine" she is saying holding my hand in her two hands "No lasting damage, but a bloody lucky escape. What was going on with you, that you ran in front of a car for Christ sakes?"

I'm not sure I dare tell her. I hesitate. Then I go for it......

'Something Marc said to me, Mum. Really upset me. I just wanted to clear things up with him. I was so distracted. Wish you could tell Dad that. *Distraught and distracted maybe but not destructive!* I was trying to get to see Marc up in Edgware, you know at his Mum's, and just talk. I was all over the place and just not paying attention, and besides it was a lousy night.

Unbelievably windy and stormy and I just didn't look properly. I saw the bus at the bus stop and went for it. All I was thinking is I've got to get to him....'

"Yes, but why did you have to see Marc so urgently? What was the great hurry?" she has her intense scorpionic gaze fixed onto me.

'He told me.....umm... he told me things I didn't want to hear......... that really freaked me out'

"Told you what?! What didn't you want to hear?!" she is pinning me down now on this one. *"For god's sake! What on earth didn't you want to hear?!"*

I realise if I tell her what I don't even want to acknowledge myself then it will inevitably alter the dynamics between all of us. Her acceptance and her approval of Marc and my father's view of him will never be quite the same again. For a second or two I consider this and then I let it out:

'He told me he didn't love me. I was really shocked. I mean not he didn't love me exactly but he isn't **in love** with me. You know all that shit..... I like you but I'm not in love with you. What the fuck am I supposed to do with that! You know stuff like **you just don't do it for me or whatever.** I feel like I'm not enough for him, or good enough for him or nearly attractive or intelligent enough or something like that.'

I am now crying and the dark pit in my gut that is spiralling me downwards is also making me gulp and gasp like a baby.

'I thought we were going to be ok, much closer, especially after spending all this time together, but we're not. We're just not.

I don't know why it hurts so much..... why does it hurt so much , Ma? I feel completely devastated.... I thought if I can see him then it'll be ok. But it will never be ok. Never!'

My mother is looking at me as if she entirely understands what I'm on about. I'm silently thinking 'how would she know? She's only ever had Dad in her life and they're still together and seem solid enough'. But she knows, she really does.

"You don't have to be everything to everybody, you really don't!" my mother is saying to me firmly and she might as well be speaking to herself too. "I can see what's happening to you and it completely breaks my heart. There are loads of people and opportunities out there! Open your eyes. And for Christ sake, just ease up on yourself a bit please?"

'What will I do, Ma? What now?'

"I don't know Sweetie" She says "Just take it easy. Let it go for now if you can. You need to get better. That arm is going to be in plaster for at least 6 weeks and you need to be a bit kinder to yourself. That bash on your head is going to take a while to heal too. That's what matters most."

I'm not really listening to what she is saying because I'm still in the pit with the monstrous despair.

'And then Dad and all his *got to get you to a shrink crap,* Ma? Going to a shrink can't make me more loveable or more beautiful can it!? It can't make Marc love me more!' I'm weeping now and she is entirely lost for words. I mean what can she say to me to make it better? My head hurts like hell and the crying isn't helping.

We're just sitting now, chain smoking her Silk Cuts and adding to the grey cloud of exhaled smoke that is forming its own biosphere above us in this hospital ward. I'll be out of here in a day or two but I'm thinking I'd rather just stay and be looked after. I want drugs, I don't care what, to anaesthetise the emotional pain because it's a whole lot worse than the physical injuries I'm carrying. That's how it feels tonight anyway.

My lost-for-words Ma sits on my hospital bed and I can sense the empathy coming from her and I wonder what's really been going down in her world that she's been hiding from us all these years?

Just as she's about to leave she says almost in passing "Anyway what about your meditation - doesn't that help? Isn't it working then?"

I can hear the bitter edge in her voice, the cynicism, and simultaneously coming from another part of her, a deep desire to make it better for me. She'd like nothing more than to ease my pain both physically and emotionally. But the fact that I now meditate and *'follow a spiritual path'* so to speak, is to her such a profound act of betrayal that she cannot countenance any beneficial possibilities. To her it is a slighting, a damning of the hard won liberal values, the rationality, the pragmatism and the humanism that she and my father so wholeheartedly ascribe to. I cannot argue with her viewpoint, because I also agree with it, yet I want to yell *Mum, honestly it isn't what you think*. I search around for a metaphor that will illustrate it better:

'Ma, it's like the Northern line going from Hampstead to Golders Green.' I say whilst she looks at me perplexed as if the head injury is making me delusional.

'Imagine yourself on the train and there's nothing to hang on to. I mean no handrails or or overhead dangly things to grab hold of or anything to stop you being shunted around. Every time the train speeds up or takes a bend a bit too fast all passengers fall over. Ok?'

She looks no less enlightened.

'Well, that's what it's like. I've now got a hand rail to hold onto. Doesn't mean the train isn't going to sometimes be driven by a speed freak, or weird things might happen on the journey, like all this crap going down with Marc, but at least I can hang on to something now. Which is much better than having absolutely nothing to stabilise me and help me keep my balance. Get it?'

I think she is alarmed at the mundane metaphor I offer, expecting something more mystical and abstract to grapple with. But she looks like she sort of gets it.

She leaves and I lie back in my trolley bed. *Where the hell is Dad?* I find myself wondering this time before my thoughts drift inevitably and relentlessly back to Marc.

- - - - - - - - - - - - - -

Hi Kit

Thanks for the latest tranch of writing and for further elucidating your relationship with your mother. You seem to be suggesting that there is indeed healing potential in this relationship which your accident has brought to the fore. I was particularly moved by the way in which you found some heartfelt and empathic points of contact bearing in mind that historically you were not that close. It almost brought tears to my eyes, but in a purely countertransferential manner, of course. She clearly cares enormously about you, even if it is sometimes hard for her to express this directly and bearing in mind that she is stoically holding the family together through one crisis after another.

Kind regards
Dr Maelstrum

PS Your mum is just great! My mother is a complete nightmare! There, I said it. I hear her voice in my head day and night, complaining about my messiness and dyspraxia. Whenever we meet she pats me down like a dog, straightening my tie, and examining my fingernails for dirt. And all done in a robotic and frighteningly detached manner! I despair!

- - - - - - - - - - - - - -

Hi Dr M

You're starting to worry. I feel there's a gigantic call (howl?) for help coming from you. I've given you details of a really good therapist so please get in touch with her asap.

Best
Kit

Dr Kniffler

(not another bloody Freudian)

I hate you! Are you satisfied now we have at last
surrendered to the roles in which we've both been cast -
A duet of 'negative therapeutic relating'
of countless shrink-wrapped generations
But I don't buy, these formulae
or potted textbook explanations

A couple of days later when my consultant is satisfied that I'm out of danger I'm discharged from hospital. Marc has stopped talking about 'moving on' for the time being. I think he's been shaken by what happened to me. On the surface, at least, things feel a bit calmer.

Once home my father wants to talk to me about going back into psychoanalysis. I was hoping he'd drop this idea, that he might be struck down by amnesia, but no such luck. He's still holding fast to the **unconscious suicide attempt hypothesis.**

For some reason he doesn't suggest Dr B and looks uncomfortable when I do. It turns out Dr B can't see me at the moment.

"Dad" I plead, "Does it have to be with another bloody Freudian then? Can't I go to a different sort of shrink this time?"

'Ok' He says in a friendly way 'I'll do my best to find you someone else. Someone good, but **not another bloody Freudian!**' He smiles and I smile too and it feels like we're on the same page.

My father has a think about it and refers me to someone from the British Independent School. I have no idea who or what this school is but at least it's not more of the same old stuff. I'm told this analyst has something to do with art therapy so it sounds a great deal more promising to my ears.

I'm on the No 13 bus going towards town. I have an appointment with Dr. Kniffler in Wimpole Street this morning. Somehow the idea of art therapy and Wimpole Street feels at odds with itself and I can't put the two together. I arrive in Dr K's plush suite and am ushered into his consulting room by his secretary. He sits starched white shirt and besuited behind a polished oak desk. None of my former shrinks have ever sat behind a desk. He has slick-backed Brylcremed hair and dark pronounced eyebrows that somehow add to the intensity of this first encounter. And I haven't seen anybody with that kind of hair in years. I am wearing the pale turquoise dressing gown and the long black skirt. He looks me up and down. In his hand is a lit cigarette and on the desk a pack of 20 Consulate Menthols. I look around the room for the art materials. I can't see any at all. No sign. For a split second I imagine Jackson Pollack let loose, anarchically flinging paint all over the flock wallpaper in this pristine stuffy consulting room and I smile. I see Dr. K covered in Jackson's splatterings. Then I ask Dr. K if I can please have one of his Consulates. He takes another drag of his, slowly blows out the smoke in a kind of provocative way, looks me in the eye and is silent. More silence. Eventually I speak:

"It doesn't seem fair that you're sitting there smoking and I've forgotten my cigarettes and you don't have the courtesy to offer me one" I say feeling upset. This is not the best start in the world.

'And tell me now, why should *I* offer *you* one?' he says coldly. 'I don't *have* to give you one. I'm not under any obligation to do so whatsoever.'

But I know if I don't have that cigarette right now I am going to get up and walk out. I think he must sense this from my uneasy body language because reluctantly he flicks the packet across the desk in my direction. I take one and lean forward to get a light from him. I'm extremely uncomfortable being in such close proximity to him. I can smell the slick-backed Brylcreme.

He's looking at me, at my clothes which aren't conventional; at the scar just above my left eyebrow which is still red and raw; at my arm in plaster. Silence.

'Do you actually *want* to be in analysis right now? You need to be clear with me, was it *your* decision to come?' He eventually asks me straight up.

"I'm not sure" I respond "to be honest it's my Dad's idea - you know, he's a shrink and anyway you probably know him. He thinks I tried to kill myself but I didn't. But aside from that I'm not feeling that great or confident right now. Had a few emotional upsets - boyfriend stuff. Sort of why my arm is in plaster...."

'Who exactly is responsible for the *payment* of your sessions?' he snarls, ignoring everything I've said.

"My parents" I respond.

'I would suggest if you're serious about this that you will work to pay for your sessions yourself. In fact, I won't see you *unless* you pay for the sessions yourself. Do you understand? Am I making myself perfectly clear?'

I'm thinking *Oh shit, I didn't see that coming.* But I say:

"Oh I see" I'm a bit taken aback by this though I can see he has a point and has got the measure of my reticence.

'You do have a job or college grant don't you?' He bellows peering down at me from behind the polished desk, making an enormous assumption.

"Well, I do domestic cleaning for a living but at the moment it's a bit difficult to clean with my right arm in plaster." I respond noting the sarcastic edge in my voice "Doesn't instil confidence in the clients either. I do bits of market research sometimes too *if* I can get the work, which isn't often."

'I suggest you think about it and *if, and only if,* you are willing to pay for your sessions, I might be willing to see you' he says bluntly, gruffly, without making eye contact and then walks towards the door holding it open for me. It's the shortest session I've ever had.

On the way home on the No 13 I do think about it. I think about my experiences so far in analysis. This guy makes the

Freudians look like friendly little puppy dogs. He is the oversized menacing Rottweiller that you do your utmost to avoid. In fact you cross the street to get out of his path if you have any sense of self preservation. Or willingly jump over that spiked 6' wall to escape his jaws. Yes, he makes the Freudians look like fluffy poodles. I try to get a sense of what Dr. K reminds me of. Yes, I've got it. It's an old fashioned, rather sadistic sergeant major. The sort you see parodied on TV. All that's missing is the twisty handlebar moustache. What was my father thinking? And why would I want to scrub all week to pay for a session of that?

Despite my misgivings, once my plaster is off, I do in fact scrub my way through each of the following 6 weeks to pay for these sessions with Dr K on a Saturday morning in Wimpole Street. Aside from covering my cigarette habit everything else I earn goes into Dr K's pocket. It gets no better. He makes unnecessary, snide comments about my appearance and if I happen to wear the same set of clothes 2 weeks in a row, you can bet your life Dr K will say something disparaging about it. As the weeks pass I genuinely begin to think he hates me and since the feeling seems to be mutual I don't understand why I am keeping up this charade. Somewhere in the back of my mind, once again, just like when I was 9 years old and seeing Fat Ankles, I recognise that I'm doing my best to please and appease my distraught parents.

Simple: I get shrunk, they feel relieved. End of story. But do they really? Who am I kidding?

Recently my father has been behaving strangely - that is, more strangely than he usually does. He seems utterly pre occupied and distant. I doubt he'd notice if I stopped seeing Dr K. I decide to give up on this ridiculous game. I say nothing to anyone and just stop turning up. I have a long lie in on Saturday mornings now. Nobody seems to notice or care, not my mother or father, Dr K or even his secretary.

Sitting less comfortably with me though, is that this painful encounter with Dr K makes me value dear Dr Beaufort's natural warm rapport all the more and I still don't get why, for some reason, I can't just go back to him.

What I cannot anticipate at this point is that I will not be going back into analysis for a very long time. This wholly unsuccessful therapeutic 'attempt' (if you can call it that) with Dr K marks the end of an era that started at 9 and has now ended at 17. I will not be in analysis again until just before I hit 30.

- - - - - - - - - - - - - -

Hi Kit
I'm concerned that if you ever let this writing see the light of day it may jeopardise our professional standing in the eyes of the public.

We have worked tirelessly to remove the stigma attached to psychotherapy and psychotherapists, to 'normalise' the process, to free it from old outdated assumptions about its efficacy and the power dynamics between therapist and patient.

However, your experiences, no matter how sincerely you express them, will I fear, add to this negative body of ideas about our beloved profession.

Yours sincerely, Dr Maelstrum

PS I stick by the above, however, I'm intrigued by your experiences...... Dr K sounds like a right bastard (reminds me a lot of my own father, in fact, especially the dark and menacing eyebrows - your description sent shivers up my spine). Actually I know all about appeasing parents, so with you on that one.

- - - - - - - - - - - - - -

Dear Dr M
Should I stop sending you my writing then? Or not? I'm not clear where you stand.

Best, Kit

What's Up with Dad?

Suddenly I'm 3 years old and I'm thinking of my dad knowing
*There's **nothing** I can do to stop him going*
Hey dad, look at me, I can do cartwheels
Hey dad, look at me I can draw pictures... really real ones
Hey dad, I'm very scared of the night..... now I'm screaming
Hey dad, tell me please, it's not really real, say it's just that I'm dreaming

My father has been attempting to give up smoking. He's doing pretty well and it must be about 8 weeks since he last had a puff. Being a hypochondriac (like me) I can understand completely why he would choose to do this. I will be following his example sometime soon, I hope.

However, this evening just after we finish dinner and I'm about to clear away the plates Dad points his finger at me and snarls aggressively "Gi' us a fag then!"

I don't quite understand him. His voice is all slurry and indistinct 'What Dad? What are you saying?'

"Gi'us a fag's wha' mm sayin, stupid!" he repeats sounding extremely annoyed.

I look at Mum and mouth silently 'What should I do?' She silently mouths back gesticulating in an exasperated fashion 'Give him a bloody cigarette for Christ's sake!'

'Dad,' I implore 'Are you sure, you were doing so well?' I feel sad.

Ezra leans over and picks up a fat orange from the fruit bowl. He throws hard it in the direction of my head and having quick reflexes, I duck. The orange missile smashes through the window just behind where my head would have been had I not moved it, shattering the glass. Undeterred he giggles in a sort of sinister way, looks at me and puts out his hand.

"Jus' gi' over" he slurs and then he grabs a cigarette from my packet of No. 6, lights it with a trembling hand and drops the lit match on the floor. He smiles a little menacingly and shuffles out of the room. We can hear him crashing about upstairs getting caught up in the furniture until finally all is quiet.

Jake is still sitting at the table motionless staring at the broken window pane.

'Dad's not feeling too good' says my mother shivering and sweeping up the chards of glass from beneath our feet whilst the night air rushes in through the gaping hole.

Yes Ma, that's stating the bleeding obvious isn't it? And this is the first time I see my father drunk.

The next day my father is extra specially friendly at first and unusually interested in all of us. Though at breakfast, as soon as

240

there is a pause in the conversation Jake grabs his toast and marmite and escapes up to his room. He's only 11 and his Dad at the best of times is a force to be reckoned with. This new side to his father is something else entirely. His unpredictability especially. Ezra asks all the right pertinent questions about what's happening in our lives but it doesn't seem as if he's hearing any of our answers. This faux interest is unnerving.

Later after he's drunk a bit more he starts to get verbally aggressive. Jake in particular seems to be on the receiving end. It's worse when Jake gravitates nervously toward our mother for protection. When he places himself in a chair or on the sofa next to her, Ezra's jealousy rears up. It is as if in this state he wants to rip them apart with his bare hands and situate himself right next to Marion and stake his claim to her. Like a very large unruly baby. It takes a massive leap in the credibility stakes to hold together the fact that this strange regressed person is also the warm, humorous if rather eccentric father I'm used to relating to. Yes, he has his super annoying analytical Tourettes moments that drive me to distraction but fundamentally he is all there. But not now.

Then I notice the other males in the household are quietly disappearing out of the picture:

Sam wisely perhaps, is in the process of moving out to live with his girlfriend, so he's really half way out of here. He's just spent a while on an organic farm near Oswestry so we're all getting used to his impending departure. *He's leaving home, bye, bye*...... Lucky Sam.

Marc who is living between our house and his mother's place keeps a very low profile and locks himself away upstairs most of the time. He seems to have had plenty of practice keeping himself well under the radar and possesses a mastery in the art of avoidance when it comes to complex family dynamics. Or at least this is how it appears to me.

Jake understandably continues to make himself scarce and is spending the evenings after school in his room, flicking through comics or flicking through the TV channels upstairs when he's certain the coast is clear. Why should he expose himself unnecessarily to his father's wrath?

The most disconcerting thing of all is that none of us can talk openly about what's happening to our father or our family. I can't talk to Ezra because he's too volatile and I'm afraid of his reactions to the truth of the situation should I actually front him with it. I can't talk to my mother because it seems there's nothing to be done or to be said - our communication is all in our silent body language and encoded facial expressions. I'm acutely aware of the 'bad' child I felt myself to be whenever I asked too many difficult, unwelcome questions. She lurks inside reminding me still to keep a lid on it.

Yes, we are all silently, unconsciously sworn to keep this secret. To say absolutely zilch to my father and to pretend that nothing untoward is taking place right under our noses if anyone else should enquire. It is extremely confusing, bewildering, and Jake in particular is struggling to make sense of it. Forget liberal values and freedom of speech. Forget honest, direct communication. It's all utterly and completely redundant now. No one will say out loud "Dad's drunk - look he's pissed as newt!" - it's all "he's under the weather" or "in a mood" or "not feeling so good" or some such phrase that minimises what is actually happening here and almost makes it palatable.

The truth is, it's completely unbearable seeing his disintegration, this transformation from the father we know and love to this peculiar stranger in our midst. And I feel terrible. The stranger he has become elicits very little emotion from me. My heart is suddenly made of ice and I feel guilty as hell that I cannot connect to feelings of compassion for him. I know underneath this survival strategy I'm absolutely heartbroken and I wonder if I've lost my beloved father forever. But I dare not let those feelings rise up in me. I guess this is how people cope, how they manage. And I wonder if this is how my mother has been coping and managing all these years. Does she feel as shut down, as repressed in her feelings as I do right now? And I don't for a minute believe this is the first time my father has been like this. I know damn well it's been going on for a while now. It's just that it's the first time he's been inebriated to this extent in front of the whole family.

And then I begin to question my father's long-standing infamous 'moods' in more depth. Yes, he gets elated and can then go rapidly downhill at other times - all very bi polar in retrospect - but where does the drinking fit? Does he drink because he's deeply unhappy or is he unhappy because he has a problem with addiction. Or is it more complicated?

Within a couple of days Ezra has deteriorated further and it is indeed getting quite a lot more complicated. Wagner's Ring Cycle blasting through the house at incredible decibels yesterday is off the agenda today. Today he's not bothering with music. Marion goes off to work at her hospital and Jake has just left for school. This morning my father is locked away in the study and I'm the only other person in the house. Even the cats are behaving oddly and slinking off into quiet, undisturbed corners. I can hear strange noises - my father is calling out but I cannot understand what for. In fact I can no longer decipher what he is saying. I don't know what to do because he's so frightening in this state. I hope and pray that all his patients have been cancelled, that no one is going to show up unexpectedly on the doorstep. Not now.

At about midday he appears. He looks terrible - exhausted, unshaven, dishevelled and barely able to stand up. He rummages around in the hall for something, opening and closing the desk drawer and getting increasingly agitated. Then he finds what he's looking for: his car keys.

'Dad' I say 'You can't drive right now. No way! Please Dad!' Ezra is having none of it. He pushes me out of the way and heads for the front door. As he's so unstable on his feet he isn't difficult to intercept. I stand in front of him with my arms out trying to create a barrier between him and the front door and he tries once more to shunt me out of his path. He is very wobbly and saying something incomprehensible whilst gesticulating. Then I get what it is. He has to *drive* down to the off licence for more vodka.

'Dad!' I shout 'Please! It's too dangerous for you to drive in this state!' What happens next is something I'm not proud of. It's something that I never thought I'd find myself doing.

I say to my father 'Give me those keys and if you hand them over, I mean **right now,** I'll go down to the bottle store and get your drink.'

Ezra immediately and compliantly hands over the keys and slinks back into his study slamming the door behind him. I walk down the road to Arthur Coopers off licence, the place where I get my No.6 and wonder what the hell I'm doing. I buy 2 bottles of vodka (on account) and make my way back up to the house. One of them I hide along with his car keys and the other I have in my hand when I knock on my father's study door. He opens it, and all I see is his shaky hand. He grabs hold of the bottle like his life depends on it, because in that moment I believe it does, and kicks shut the door.

I sit on the stairs and wait for what feels like an eternity for my mother to get back from work, which she does earlier than usual. As soon as she walks through the door I confess all to her. She doesn't even have time to take her coat off.

"Mum, I did something terrible today. I bought more vodka for Dad" I blurt out.

My mother is totally understanding. 'What's happening with him?' She asks

"I dunno. He's in the study. Haven't heard a peep out of him for hours now. I'm sorry Ma I didn't know what to do. I really didn't. Fucking hell, he wanted to drive the car! I've hidden his car keys and another bottle of vodka behind that rubber plant. I don't know why I bought 2 bottles! Did I do something really awful today, be honest with me?"

'No, of course not' says my mother emphatically 'what else could you do? He would have found a way to keep drinking or else done some terrible damage if he'd gone out in the car.'

Later Marion finds my father semi conscious lying face down on the carpet in his study. She calls me over to his side to help move him.

'We have to get him to hospital **now**!' she says and I can feel the absolute urgency in her voice.

We somehow manage, though I don't know how, to bundle him into the car and deliver him to Charing Cross hospital, my mother driving while I'm in the back with Ezra. If we were to get stopped by the police now my mother would get booked for drunk driving. The alcoholic fumes emanating from my father which we are currently breathing in could cause an explosion. When we arrive at Charing Cross we are met by a team of nurses. It seems they know exactly what to do. I have a sneaking suspicion he's been in here before.

When we get home Jake asks what's going on.

'Dad's not very well' says my mother using one of the stock euphemisms from the list. 'He's going to be in hospital for a bit.'

"Oh" says Jake and gets on with what ever he's doing.

Later the house is ghostly quiet. Marion is smoking and playing Solitaire upstairs in the TV room but the TV isn't on. Jake is in his room. I go into the TV room and sit with her. She doesn't seem to want to speak. I make us some tea and bring it upstairs.

"What now Ma?" I say eventually

'They'll dry him out. You know, detox him. He's terrified of hospitals.' She says focussing on the Solitaire whilst speaking and I detect a muffled sob of desperation just behind her words.

"Why's that?"

'Years ago he had a bad experience. They detoxed him too quickly. He's never trusted them since.'

I'm thinking *years ago? How many years ago?*

"Mum! How many years ago! How long as this been going on?" I am raising my voice slightly and at the same time I don't mean to add to my mother's misery. I shut up and let her tell me:

'Your Dad had a series of alcoholic breakdowns when we went back to South Africa when you and Sam were really little, after Dad's analytical training. You would only have been about 2 or 3. Have you got any memories of us in Cape Town?'

"Yeah Ma" I say "I do, you know. Very bright snap shots of certain things - like the bluebottles on the beach. Like being told I'd go to jail if I picked the roses."

She looks at me strangely 'What? Oh you mean Joseph, the gardener? He was a bit of a nutter, a paranoid schizophrenic, we thought.'

Then she goes on:

'It was a disastrous time for us all. Apart from Dad's breakdowns, which were difficult enough, the family was involved in a serious car crash where this truck was completely at fault. The driver shunted us off the road. This had nothing to do with your father drinking. He was sober at the time. Our car was turned over; it was upside down in a ditch when we were found. It's amazing we escaped with so few injuries. I had a few cracked ribs and that was about it. Everyone else, you and Sam, Dad, were miraculously unhurt. The shit of a driver who was a farmer had a personal connection, was all very chummy with the local police who, of course, protected him. He never went to court for it. He should have been prosecuted and made to take responsibility for what he did. It was horrific that he got away with it, scott free.'

"Fucking bastards" I say, stunned by her revelations.

She continues:

'It wasn't an easy time for us, obviously. We were testing out whether we could make a go of it back in Cape Town. Your father in particular developed a lasting fear, a distrust of authority in general. A loathing, really. Of the police, of course, and there were plenty of other political and idealogical reasons to distrust the SA police, as you well know.'

"Blimey Ma!" I say revisiting past events in my mind because I'm remembering my father sidling up to the police when I got arrested. It might explain his weird, out of character compliance if he was that afraid of them.

'But he also became very frightened of hospitals when we were in Cape Town this time. He ended up having a seizure, you know a fit, during a badly handled period of detoxification. If they dry you out too quickly, that's what happens. So, it was pretty much a disaster. Well, an absolute disaster really. So we came back to live in London after about 18 months hoping it would work out for us here. And mostly it has, hasn't it?' She says looking at me almost quizzically, somehow wanting my approval and I nod.

'But I'm glad we left anyway, even without all the awful things that happened. It would never have worked out for us in SA, not at that time.' And I know she's talking about the era, apartheid, and the unremitting ghastliness of that.

Then she says 'Maybe don't tell Jake what I've said, I think he's a bit too young to understand'.

Apart from something very vague about a car crash, my mother has never told me any of this before. I attempt to pull these newly revealed strands together in my mind. I'm trying to take in all this information. I clearly remember my father's version of why we didn't stay on in SA. It was nothing remotely like the one I've just heard from my mother. His version was that they didn't have a clue what psychoanalysis was in Cape Town at that time, which would have been mid/ late 1950's, so therefore he couldn't establish a practice there. I'm guessing this was true, as well.

Marion's revelations begin to make sense of what's going on now, but they don't help get to the heart of **why** my father is so unhappy, so self destructive in the first place. This other 'him', this desperate person who has suddenly appeared in our midst - what's that all about, I'm thinking, but I don't probe my poor Ma any further, not tonight.

My mother is now very silent and even the Solitaire can't hold her attention. She has this way of looking contained and together, no matter what's going on. She lights another cigarette and goes to check on Jake. I'm not sure where Marc is, probably laying low somewhere in the house. Perhaps wisely, he's standing well clear of the blue touchpaper tonight. I take myself off to bed but cannot sleep at all. My mind is in overdrive.

I have so many unanswered questions like, for example, how often does this happen? I mean once in a blue moon or 10 times a year, or what? Why is Dad so depressed? What's it like for my mother to be confronted with all of this? How does she cope? Do they talk openly together about it or pretend that nothing is going down? Then I try to imagine my parents young and in love, and optimistic. And so on and so forth.

Hi Dad

A few weeks later I accompany my mother to Charing Cross Hospital to collect Ezra. He's been in detox for about 3 weeks now. We go into the waiting area and through the glass partition

I can see him sitting in the lounge with a few of the other patients chatting. It looks like he's holding court. He smiles at my mother and me. He looks genuinely happy to see us and waves.

"Hi Dad" I say a little tentatively "How're you doing?"

'Hi Diabolical' he replies using the name he gave me when I was about 2 or maybe even younger. He hasn't called me that in years.

My mother seems busy talking to doctors and I'm guessing sorting out the official bits and pieces to do with him being discharged.

"What's it been like in here, Dad?" I say because I'm not so certain anymore what I can and can't say to him. *Though what a part of me would very much like to say is "**I didn't realise you were an alcoholic, Dad**" but I don't say that.*

'I've been taking group therapy sessions' he says 'It's been a really interesting process. Some of the patients have incredible stories and backgrounds....'

I've stopped listening now and I'm thinking *What? He's been **taking** group therapy sessions?*

"D'you mean participating in group therapy sessions, Dad? I mean taking part in them?"

'No, silly!' he says affectionately 'I've organised these sessions for everyone and I've been taking them myself. I thought that's something I can offer. I think some people have really benefitted....'

"Oh, that's interesting!" I say and at one level I'm fascinated, intrigued that he would do this and at another I'm alarmed that he cannot just let himself be the patient, not the professional right now. But I'm so relieved that my father has been restored to some semblance of the man I used to know that I don't go there. I'm thinking ***thank god, I can feel for you again.*** That shut down, frozen place where I've been hiding all these weeks seems at last to have thawed out around me and all I feel is love for him, for my mother, for all of us. So the very last thing I want to do right now is rub his denial in his face.

My mother appears with a parcel of pharmaceuticals under her arm and we drive home with my father filling us in on his free NHS group therapy service for addicts and alcoholics.

- - - - - - - - - - - - - -

```
Hi Kit
Your father is an extraordinary and highly complex
human being. Despite all his problems he still
wants to help! I agree, no one wants to disturb
the  hard  earned  peace.  All  this  co-dependent
nonsense really grates. Who came up with the
theory? I say 'put up and shut up' !

Kind regards
Dr M

PS Just reminding you too, I'm number one admirer
when it comes to your mother ! What a heroine !!
Whereas with mine...... well you can imagine (the
fuss!)
```

- - - - - - - - - - - - - -

```
Hi Dr M
Did you ever get around to calling the therapist I
suggested for you? If not, you need to get your
act together. I can give you the number of a great
supervisor too if you need?

Best
Kit
```

Reprieve

The days following Ezra's return from hospital are calm. It's as if nothing much has happened. I suspect he is strongly medicated. He is in good spirits - we don't talk about spirits of the other sort. Not at all. He clearly knows that I know, but once again we don't mention 'it'. Obviously my mother knows that I know but the portal to this other reality is now shut. Out of bounds. We are behaving like amnesiacs. What am I supposed to do with the fact that I have firstly, witnessed 'it' with my own eyes and bought him supplies, secondly she has filled me in on the history in no uncertain terms. And finally, I remind myself, I've been with her to deliver and collect my father from hospital? It feels quite crazy that I have to keep remembering these facts because the pull to obliterate them from my memory banks is so overwhelmingly powerful. It is as if we've *never* talked about 'it' suddenly. And as if I wasn't even *there* when it all unfolded.

So we honour our silent agreement because to talk, to blurt out the obvious, is either an act of disloyalty or an act of utter stupidity. Even if all the books ever written about co-dependence would argue the opposite case. The fragile peace is too delicate, too desired to upset. So why would I want to put the boot in? But it's impossible to imagine that this will never happen again. It's only a matter of time. Our collective, consensual denial can never entirely banish that thought so it floats around creating a hyper vigilance in all of us. We're constantly on the look out for 'signs' of my father's impending descent.

Meanwhile, Bill Evans and Theolonius Monk are back on the turntable which is no bad sign and an indication that a tentative peace has been restored.

I start thinking differently, more reflectively, about my father in an attempt to understand him better: His parents, his background, because somehow he carries such a deep, soul destroying despair it has to have come from somewhere, surely? I think about my paternal grandparents Fanny and Charlie. Charlie who is a retired fishmonger is very nearly stone deaf and holds his shaky hands behind his back most of the time, looking confused, muttering and nodding. Fanny screams at him so he can hear her, or does she just scream because she's frustrated as hell with him? This has been going on for decades. Fanny is a bold, powerful woman (domineering might be a more accurate description) with large expressive eyes and full downturned mouth. Larger than life might be another description and my first hand experience of Fanny and Charlie comes approximately every other year when they ship themselves over on the Union Castle and stay for a couple of months in the summer. My father looks just like his mother when he's in a mood.

There are sad stories in the family of Fanny having lost a baby at full term before my father, her only surviving child, was born in 1924. So neurotic was she about the survival of this second child that she took his temperature everyday and stuffed him full of food thus ensuring that he had a weight problem by the time he reached puberty. My father had had diptheria when he was very young so Fanny's anxieties weren't baseless. I can fully appreciate why she might be overprotective. My father needless to say is a lifelong hypochondriac.

Some of Ezra's more entrenched ideas start to come back to me. One of them, one of his pet theories is that no one ever emigrates for political, social or economic reasons. Not really. Dig a little deeper and you'll discover the one and only 'real' reason is to escape the clutches of their parents. And 'don't be fooled' he would interject just to add weight to this hypothesis, even if it looks like something else, it isn't. Obviously this is his story. And obviously moving back to the place of his birth had been an unmitigated disaster. Neither were the grandparents' periodic visits devoid of tension either.

The evenings spent with them consist of a great deal of tedious tea drinking, chain smoking and card games. They also consist of avoiding certain subjects such as apartheid SA and all talk of politics generally. I barely remember much else, apart from the awkward feelings, embarrassing snippets of conversation and a fascination with the slippage of Granny Fanny's hair piece. I wonder if it might have been easier to bond with these grandparents had the massive, ever growing chasm between the generations - my parents and theirs - not been so acutely and tangibly evident to all present.

My father has the legitimate excuse of his work to ease the tension of us all holed up together in the house. He can escape to the sanctity of his consulting room and he rarely finishes work before 8pm. Marion works full time now and therefore is out until about 7 pm each evening. Though some evenings you can catch her sitting in the car listening to Radio 4 delaying the inevitable. That leaves me and Jake mainly wandering the corridors in a state of active avoidance, although it is more the embarrassment of not knowing how to make 'safe' conversation with my grandparents that creates the most discomfort.

My father has a thing about what he calls 'castrating or emasculating women'. For some reason Glenda Jackson in *Women in Love* (DH Lawrence / Ken Russell film, 1969) seems to epitomise this for him. He continues to hate ball breaking Glenda regardless of the roles she plays. He cannot forgive her for Gudrun and I guess imagines himself walking out into the freezing night, heartbroken and tormented, to die a lonely, dejected death on a snowy alpine mountainside much as Gerald (Oliver Reed) did. There are other women my father adores. He loves the jazz singers Anita O'Day and Ella and Billy of course, and Blossom Dearie (who we see at Ronnie Scott's Jazz venue on a regular basis). He's a fan of Dusty. He adores Maria Callas and

Kathleen Ferrier but cannot stand Kiri te Kanawa. On the political spectrum he admires Shirley Williams and Barbara Castle and he will naturally detest Margaret Thatcher when she appears on the scene even more than he detests Glenda (though not for her politics - Glenda's that is). I think he likes Barbara Streisand which is slightly confusing and now I'm not too sure I can see a logic to the pattern. Whatever or whoever he likes, he likes with all his heart and whenever he hates he does so with full, unbridled conviction. No half measures. He loves my mother. I'm not so sure I entirely understand what he feels about his own.

Later this year, however, it will be the turn of my maternal grandfather, Aaron, to visit which brings with it its own challenges. But just before he does Sam and I make a discovery......

Oh..... and

Riders On The Storm...

One weekday afternoon a month or so after Dad's hospitalisation, Sam and I are both at home rummaging around looking for cigarettes. Our family have a peculiar arrangement with certain consumables. We have a floor to ceiling storage cupboard in the corridor leading to the kitchen that has unofficially been named the Third World War cupboard. It's full to the brim with emergency foodstuffs should there suddenly be a need. We once counted 18 jars of supermarket strawberry jam and almost as many decades old cans of butter beans, lychees and guavas and then dozens of tins (yes, tins for some reason) of apricot and gooseberry jams from South Africa. It is crammed full of the edibles you're most unlikely to need in an emergency. Why my mother feels it necessary to stock pile this stuff is beyond comprehension. However, stashed away in other places - the back of the kitchen drawer amongst the tea towels and loose leaf recipes, underneath the disintegrating papers and ancient letters in the hall drawer and in Ezra's study drawer are secret stashes of cigarettes and Cote d'Or praline chocolate. This is where we head to when we run out of the essentials.

Sam and I have sifted through the kitchen drawer and excavated the contents of the hall drawer without finding anything worth smoking. In fact one of the items we unearth in the process turns out to be the short chestnut ladies wig that Sam has used to pile his wild afro hair beneath for school.

"Christ!" says Sam "My head got so bloody sweaty in that thing! Pretty fantastic of Dad though to agree to let me have it. Y'know it started a trend? There was absolutely nothing they could do about it, the teachers, that is. It was hilarious!"

'Yeah, you looked pretty damn strange in it' I reply, also trying to imagine how it felt 'But not everyone had all that long, springy hair to squash into a hideous wig! Must have been *so* damn itchy.'

"God, it's revolting!" says Sam examining it, smelling it and chucking it back into the drawer looking disgusted.

We still haven't had much success in our cigarette search and as the withdrawal symptoms and crabby mood intensifies we progress onto Ezra's study desk. He is out working at one of his clinics and not expected back until the early evening. Even so we are slightly trepidacious although this is certainly not the first time we've raided his supplies. The desk drawer itself is a bit stiff and takes some jiggling to get open. In the process we dislodge a couple of dark red John Player's packs from its far recesses, one of which is already open. That makes it a whole lot easier as our dear father is unlikely to notice a couple of missing cigarettes, whereas he would most certainly notice the disappearance of a whole pack. But in our rummaging around we dislodge and unearth something else that we were not expecting to find. Lying loose in the drawer are a number of A5 grainy but professional looking black and white photographs. At first, as they are upside down, it's unclear what they are of. Very soon it is all too clear what they are of. Sam looks at me and I look at him. I say "Oh". Sam says 'Oops'. We tentatively examine the photos, touching just their edges and avoiding leaving greasy finger marks on them, as if we are in a crime scene investigation. Next we swap and Sam says 'Oh' in a curious sort of way and I say "Oops" in a seriously we shouldn't be doing this sort of way because it feels like an invasion of my father's privacy. The photographs are of young, good looking, half dressed men with gigantic erections. The Oh and the Oops are said in such a way that we both recognise a truth has been revealed, the beans have been spilled and everything falls into stark but staggeringly clear perspective:

Sam says 'Did you know?'

I say "Did you?"

Sam says 'No'

I say "Nope".

We guiltily shove everything back into the drawer though en route can't help but notice a small pile of calling cards with names such as 'Adam's Escorts' written upon them.

Sam says 'Umm'.

I say "Err...... lets try and leave things as we found them."

Which we proceed to do as painstakingly and meticulously as we can. We tiptoe out of the study checking that we are alone even though it's obvious no one else is in the house and then uncomfortably smoke our stolen cigarettes at the kitchen table.

The main question hovering over us and our accidental discovery is, naturally, who knows what? And uppermost in my mind is *does my mother know?* We carry on smoking and thinking, letting the new information settle as much as is possible. My thoughts are going "Dad, men?" and then "Men and Dad, really?" I contemplate this reality as the spontaneous process of reviewing and rewriting events of the past to fit with current revelations automatically clicks into place. Next I try to connect to what I'm feeling about my father. I genuinely cannot make it out. All I know is it's as if I'm holding my breath. My throat is dry as a bone. Since my father has always been full of surprises maybe this is just another one of them? And maybe I am in shock because my feelings are so muted and subdued - the ever familiar numbness is descending fast, imperceptibly spreading its anaesthetic properties all over my normal feeling state. My thoughts rest again with my introverted, reserved mother and despite the anaesthesia I feel waves of empathy and sadness for her irrespective of whether or not she 'knows'. And I feel dread on her behalf.

In the weeks that followed I found myself reverting back to cloud gazing, very much as I had done at school in the later days. Distracted and disconnected. The early new year sky arrived with mid afternoon sunsets projected onto blocks of dense greyness. Sometimes they would be scattered with wispy clouds catching the pinky orange sun low on the city skyline. In that mix I saw endless scared rabbits and hares dashing across the skyscape, running for their lives. Not safe, most certainly insecure and disappearing before they could be trapped and eaten alive. I started thinking about us in similar terms; it was an appropriate metaphor for the state of anxiety ridden suspension we found ourselves in: My father on the run from a huge part of himself, his hidden identity. My mother on the run from her stultifying low sense of self esteem and misplaced feelings of shame, whilst trying to keep us all afloat in this impossible situation. If I was on the run it would inevitably be from my bodily fears and anxieties, and the inescapable feeling that I was about to be left any second now by Marc.

I sensed then my familiarity with the concept of abandonment - as in 'being left'. As if I knew it intimately in my blood and body - it was written into my DNA. It occurred to me then, that the '*disappearing man*' as a living dynamic process felt as familiar as my own reflection in the mirror. I just hadn't ever noticed it before.

Then I thought about Jake & Sam and obviously there were Dad's unpredictable mood swings and drinking habits that any vaguely self respecting kid would want to run a mile from. Jake was visibly afraid of him. But it wasn't that simple or clear cut. We were all on the run from the not-so-secret Secret. Then I wondered once more about Marc. There was so much more in his background worthy of a desire to escape yet he seemed - at least outwardly - considerably more self assured than the rest of us and in possession of a tangible sense of direction. How the hell did he do it?

The sky that January kept turning a vicious red, marked by thin skeleton trees hanging onto their fragile bits of branch and winter bud. Soon a corridor of freezing north easterlies would rip through those brittle unprotected branches but it was impossible to predict when that was going to happen. Just before night came that same sky oozed a bile yellow Rothko like band of colour squashed beneath the hanging grey winter nimbus. The nervous rabbits were either in hiding or had become someone's dinner. Then the backdrop turned a sullen, bad tempered black. Did Sam feel as sick and scared as I did, I found myself wondering?

Marc Comes Up with a Plan

River Deep, Mountain High

Running concurrently with recent revelations the state of things between Marc and myself seemed to have taken a slightly different turn. Since starting to meditate the desire to up sticks and move on has a newfound sense of direction and purpose. Marc now plans to do some extensive travelling and exploring culminating in a spiritual festival in New Delhi later that year in November. He wants to take about a year out to travel there and back overland. As the early spring approaches he begins to formulate travel plans that will take him overland through Europe and Asia starting out in the late summer months. We begin to discuss the possibility (though it is only that and I can sense some ambivalence from both of us) of my meeting up with him out in Delhi for the festival. Though I cannot quite envisage arriving in Delhi alone (never having flown, at all, anywhere, ever) the thought is pacifying to my dependent or perhaps emerging co-dependent self. We do now have a shared interest in 'consciousness expansion' ideas and a meditation practice in common. I think we both share too a degree of excitement about what might happen next - the potential of the as yet 'unknown' energies at work.

This unexpected optimism shapes my thoughts and cuts through the habitual position that the familiar pit of nameless anxiety has historically occupied. Perhaps we are tapping into a collective 'something' that is ultimately more important than our personal relationship, dare I think it? The current situation feels to me a whole lot better than it used to, mostly though, because I'm not simply waiting passively to be abandoned and wondering at exactly what point 'it' is inevitably going to happen. I know exactly when it will happen now (when Marc leaves in the summer) and the fact that it might not signify 'the absolute end' should we meet up later, has a calming and soothing effect naturally on my insecure self.

Meanwhile that Easter we take a trip out to St.Pierre to 'build and fix things'. Marc has offered to work on the apartment and modernise some of M. Gregoire's less well constructed pieces of carpentry and cabinet making. He does have an engineering qualification amongst a variety of other talents. And though they (the pieces of carpentry that is) look beautiful (as in the image of their maker, M. Gregoire) they are beginning to come rather drastically apart (in parallel perhaps with Gregoire's complex personal life which is going in a similar direction). In a neighbouring Alpes Maritime village called Bezudun, Georgina's parents are involved in a protracted legal battle with dear M.

Gregoire since their own property, bought in similar circumstances to ours, has begun to topple over the edge of a cliff - it is literally falling apart (and over). Gregoire, meanwhile, has been fighting tooth and nail to divest himself of any responsibility for its collapse.

It is quite tragic witnessing what has become of Georgina's family's sad *maison*. No amount of attention to artistic detail, M. Gregoire's forte and real interest, can curtail its inevitable slide down the mountainside. Subsidence is the least of their worries. Soon their property will cease to exist at all. Visiting it in its dying days is sorrowful indeed. The traditional yellow ochre, hand-crafted floor tiles, the stone fireplaces, the ancient oak beams and curvy wrought iron railings cling on for dear life as gigantic floor to ceiling cracks forge a path up from the earth through the damp and peeling walls, ripping apart the bricks, mortar and everything else. Any day now it will completely *disparu* in a cloud of rubble and dust. *Mon dieu.* Gregoire's long suffering wife is apoplectic with fury at her husband's normally benign incompetence though that in itself isn't even remotely the origin of her perpetual dissatisfaction and angry furrowed brow. Her husband it seems, has numerous problems with 'distractions' of a different sort.

In our apartment in neighbouring St.Pierre the situation is not quite as alarming. We just need a few more cupboards and a spot of renovation to the existing woodwork. Marc and I had been working flat out in London to raise enough money for him to travel, and for me to have the choice should I decide to take the trip out East. I was starting to feel an inverted sense of pride, thinking that maybe one day I would be able to say I *scrubbed* my way to India, courtesy of Haleans domestic cleaning agency and the clients I had nicked from them. There was something satisfyingly masochistic about that idea. Marc had been offered a number of market research projects as well, that kept us occupied, focussed and above all, earning. On the agenda had been the inevitable processed meat, beer too this time and for some strange reason we'd found ourselves researching public opinion on undersea cables and their impact on the fishing industry. Neither of us were currently eating meat or fish nor drinking much beer, but that was par for the course in our increasingly bizarre and oppositional relationship with the world of market research. It seemed inconceivable that we might some day work on a product that we actually consumed ourselves. Small chance.

My parents were only too grateful to pay Marc to work on our French property. (They had initially made a misguided effort to use the local builders and artisans whenever they could, but recognised early on that in fact they were not the least bit interested.) So we ventured forth by car into the mountains with Marion, Ezra and Jake that Easter on the proverbial 'working holiday'.

Ten days or so later, after the project has been completed Marc and I set off up the mountain to catch a ride home via the Mont Blanc tunnel heading towards Basel in Switzerland where he has friends. He tells me it will take about 3 days hitching to get there. It's a little crazy, just a bit, as the newly fallen snow is beginning to settle and the mountain passes around St.Pierre are extremely narrow and treacherous when icy. It doesn't stop us flagging down a ride in an Italian articulated lorry that is heading northbound towards Turin. This is one of the scariest experiences of my life. As I sit in the passenger seat by the window, the roadside and the grassy snow-covered verge are obscured from my line of vision. All that I see is a precipitous drop deep into the craggy, rock-strewn river valley far below as we slide round the tight hairpins on this single-lane, ascending pass. I fear if I lean over a little too far this truck will plunge into the abyss and that will be it. I don't lean, I don't look, I don't dare. I hold my breath, I pray. I compulsively press my foot down onto a phantom braking system that gives the illusion of some vestige of control where there is absolutely none. I cannot stop myself or my foot or my knuckles from turning a whiter shade of pale.

It occurs to me that this is something of a trial run in preparation for heading out East later in the year if I've got the nerve: The plan thus far (if I could get it together to fly out to Delhi) would be for us to explore India and then travel back home overland eventually which would take us across the scary, almost mythological Khyber Pass to name but one small section of the journey. Naturally I wonder if I'll have the guts to go through with it or whether I'll bottle out. We'll see.

My Father, My Mother, My Grandfather

(& The 'Patient')

Listen, Do You Wanna Know a Secret?

A bit later that spring of 1972 just after my 18th birthday, it's my grandfather Aaron who boards the Union Castle liner in Cape Town bound for Southampton. My mother, not being much of a 'morning person', decides to travel down the evening before her father's ship is due in and stay overnight in a hotel near the port in Southampton. My father, however, has been hovering at that perilous edge which normally signifies that he is about to go under. All the indications are there which I will not bore you with. I cannot quite imagine my mother's dilemma as she heads off for the south coast knowing not what she will be met with on her return. I am left to 'manage' Ezra and, should it prove necessary, to attempt a futile exercise in damage limitation which is nigh on impossible when he is utterly fixated on getting plastered the minute she is out of sight.

He has already purchased the regulation stash of vodka ahead of time. He locks himself into the study and drinks solidly for the latter part of the afternoon and into the early evening accompanied by Wagner's ring cycle, and on this particular occasion, some gloomy, doom-ridden symphony courtesy of Shostakovitch. At some point the bell rings, the music stops dead and my father stumbles to the front door before the patient can be intercepted. I feel bad. Worse than bad, I feel terrible. Part of the unspoken role, damage limitation duties, is to protect him professionally if humanly possible. This I cannot do if he forgets to cancel his wretched patients or he encounters them before they can be diverted and fobbed off with a plausible excuse of some sort or another (normally that he suddenly has 'bronchitis').

A part of me wants to phone my mother and beg for her help and advice but what can she possibly do from afar? Another part of me wants to protect her, knowing she has to caretake my elderly grandfather on his arrival after a 2 week sea voyage and all that that entails. Simultaneously I am furious with my father and yet apologetic and guilty that I feel so damn angry and above all, inept. This time though something is different.

My father tells me through slurred and almost incoherent speech what his plans are for the evening:

'I'm going to be seeing my patient in the bedroom' he states holding onto the bannister to steady himself. I have to ask him to repeat this as at first I cannot understand what he is saying. He says it again.

I take it in and I believe him. Ezra. Patient. Bedroom. For a moment it all sounds quite plausible. Ok, he is seeing the patient in the bedroom. So what? Maybe the patient is very, very tired

269

and needs to lie down? Poor weary patient, I am thinking, forgetting of course that there is, always has been, a couch in the study anyway. *My father becomes, in my child mind, the adult who knows what he is doing. I am the child who does not understand, cannot understand and longs to trust the adult. I am the child who believes absolutely that adults know best.* Stuck in this infantile trance I wholly accept what my father tells me until the spell is broken by the loud moaning sounds coming from the bedroom. I hear two male voices and one of them is Ezra's. The other I do not recognise.

On the upstairs landing by the bedroom door there are clothes strewn across the floor. There is a leather jacket. A white tee shirt. Crumpled inside out jeans. Biker boots. The moaning continues. Eventually, though it takes far far longer than it should, I get that this isn't a patient. My naivety is stunning to behold. Then I sit and wait it out in the kitchen. Jake is watching TV with the volume turned up high enough to drown out the noises coming from the parental bedroom. I don't have any idea where Marc is tonight. I wait until eventually I hear the front door close and notice the pile of clothes has gone from the hallway. My father appears and attempts shakily to normalise the fact once again that he has seen 'the patient' in the wrong room. Then he takes himself back to bed for the rest of the night.

I can't sleep because my mother on her return will inevitably ask me what's been going on. What state will my father be in by morning too? And my grandfather? Yes, my grandfather. He's no idiot.

My mother returns with Aaron mid morning the next day. Unloading suitcases from the car, she asks me how my father's doing. Before I answer, my grandfather smiling, presents us with two large crates of oranges and almost ripe avocados that he has brought for us all the way from the sunny Cape. I feel strangely moved, touched that he has bothered. He looks so proud and pleased. He cups my face in his hands, squeezes hard and says 'Bubala...' He kisses my forehead. He has greeted me like this since I was a baby.

My poor unwitting grandfather has arrived at the worst time imaginable. My mother asks me yet again about my father. I wish she would stop it.

Downstairs Aaron makes buttered toast with avocado for Jake and does the face squeezy ritual with him too. Upstairs in the TV room my mother and I smoke her Silk Cuts while she waits for me to speak:

"Ummm..... Ma, Mum..... ?" I mumble nervously..

'Yes? What? Tell me. Just tell me what's happening with Dad?' (He is still in bed upstairs, patients - real ones, that is - cancelled.)

'He's obviously been drinking, hasn't he?' she states looking at me straight on but her hand is trembling just a tiny bit and her tea is spilling onto the lino.

"Yes, he has Mum. But not just that....... other strange things have been happening" I find myself saying.

'Other strange things? People?'

"Not people exactly. *Person"* I 'fess up.

And before I can elaborate she says almost whispering 'So you know?'

I say "Yes, I know."

She looks at me 'How long have you known?'

"Not long, Ma. Not long." I say to her feeling incredibly sad for her yet struggling to find adequate words that might acknowledge and appreciate everything she holds together for us all.

"Not long, but we - Sam and me - we found pictures in Dad's desk, you know, photos, when we ran out of fags, I mean cigarettes" I tell her, ashamed of the insensitive, unintentional pun that has spewed forth from my lips.

"I'm sorry Mum. I'm really sorry. I didn't know what to do. I didn't know if you knew. Didn't know how to talk to you about it."

'So Sam knows too?' she says looking utterly defeated and mortified.

"Yes, he knows too Ma".

The more I say the more I seem to be drawing in the clouds of shame and humiliation around her. It is almost as if my father's indiscretion becomes entirely hers or if not hers exactly, then somehow her responsibility. As if she personally has something to do with it, when clearly she does not. Whatever it is that he is living out and grappling with undoubtedly pre dates their own fateful meeting by decades. Yet there is no relief in these revelations, not for her or for me right now. None whatsoever.

'Ok, sweetie, I'm just so sorry you had to find out like this' she says clearly troubled by how I might be dealing with this new

272

information. It makes me want to weep for her. But conversely I also want to shake her and throw the unspoken concern back in her direction. I want to say:

*'For fuck's sake Ma! How the hell are **you** dealing with this!'*

Instead I say "I'm sorry too Ma. I'm sorry I couldn't stop it happening just now. I almost called you at the hotel last night but I didn't in the end - I couldn't see how that would help."

'No, it's ok. We'll see how Dad is later. Let him sleep it off' She says, taking one of my grandfather's suitcases to the spare room where he'll be staying for the next couple of months. She is so composed and dignified even when utterly crushed and humiliated. She is the very antithesis of that self referring, stereotypical fussy Jewish mother/martyr. In that moment, and in the many moments like this to follow, I discover the depth of respect I have and will continue have for my mother. She has bucket loads of integrity. I only hope that one day, somehow my dear Ma will find her way out of this hellhole. When it's like this, anyway.

Ezra sleeps 'it' off, sort of. When he appears a few hours later he is dishevelled but 'friendly', in that faux friendly, over-enquiring manner that has by now become a recognisable feature in the pattern of his drinking. I cannot envisage how we will manage my desperate, struggling father in this fragile state of imminent descent with my grandfather now in the house, possibly bearing witness as to what really goes down around here. I cannot envisage it, but we do, we do manage because, well, this family has become pretty damn good and adept at 'managing' - whatever the hell that is starting to look like.

Now that Marion knows that I know, something in me is released to ponder the imponderables. Separating out the elements: I find no issue in principle with the sexuality part at all, why would I with my liberal, permissive upbringing? Excepting for the fact that it causes my mother great anguish and that it reveals itself only when an injurious amount of alcohol acts as the disinhibiting factor. It scares me that my father is willing (intentionally or not) to risk everything personally and professionally. But it is as if this other self wants to be known, to be revealed (exposed even) and it simply will not be repressed. The de-criminalisation of homosexual acts between consenting adults (albeit those over the age of 21) in relative terms has only just taken place in the UK (1967). More recently though, in 1969, an amendment to the so-called 'immorality act' has now prohibited what they term erotic conduct between 2 or more people of the same sex in SA legislation. I try to imagine what it might have been like to be raised in the conservative, right wing, white SA of my parents' youth, especially if you happen to be a gay or bi-sexual man, let alone a member of the communist party as my father had been too. The mere idea evokes chilling persecutory sensations that run in icy rivers up and down my spine. Then as a follow-on my thoughts turn to Europe mid 20th century and the rest is, well, history.

Pulling my focus back to the personal I wonder not just who this complicated and tormented being, my father, really is but who he might actually be if he legitimately allowed himself. To what extent does he or does he not relate to the world through the secret of his not so hidden identity? I find myself wondering too what he honestly feels about women, other than the 'castrating' Glenda Jackson/Gudrun archetype that we already know about. What does he feel about the feminine? From a self centred perspective I am thinking *so what does he feel about me, his daughter, then*? Next I consider my parents' relationship. They have an undeniably powerful bond. Ezra & Marion. There's nothing fake or disingenuous about that. I have witnessed the affection, physically too, between them often. But what is the nature of that bond? At what point in time did my mother come t o *'know'*? Such an innocuous little word that betrays its own significance. Once again there is an invisible barrier standing between us: I don't feel I have permission to talk to her about it. I fear that something significantly more destructive will happen should I open my mouth and name the obvious. And naturally, the question of whether or not, or at what point might my father might need to be hospitalised once again dominates. And so on ad infinitum.

Then something a bit different and unexpected happens. My father seems to want to pull himself back from the brink this time. His psychiatrist prescribes a drug called Antabuse as a preventative measure. This now means if he continues to drink he will experience a plethora of truly ghastly nauseating symptoms as a result of the combustible reaction of this drug with any alcohol, should it be present, in his system. One day my father will experiment and discover that he can in fact drink whilst taking Antabuse after all, such is the robust nature of his steely constitution. Right now, however, he doesn't yet know this.

- - - - - - - - - - - - - - -

Hello Kit
Just to let you know in advance, I will be taking a sabbatical as soon as I can organise my life accordingly.

Kind regards
Dr M

PS This latest revelation has completely pulled the rug out. Your father's homoerotic shenanigans have been staring me in the face all along and I failed to pick up the signs. I am clearly not fit to practice.

PPS Actually when I say 'sabbatical' it is my way of suggesting that I will most likely be retiring in the very near future.

PPPS My sense of Self, my identity personal and professional has been of late somewhat challenged. I no longer know what I am about, what matters any more - I could go on but this is not the time nor the place. Apologies.

- - - - - - - - - - - - - -

Hi Dr M

Try not to beat yourself up! All this self flagellation won't achieve a thing. You really do need to sort out the superego injunctions dominating your sense of self. Your father has a lot to answer for. As for your mother........ (Dial that therapist's number, won't you?)

Best
Kit

Conversation with my Father

(Summer of '72)

"Hi Diabolical" my father says with a grin on his face "Can I have a word? Come in, sit down a minute. D'you want a cigarette?"

'Ta, Dad' I say sitting on the couch in his study lighting up one of his John Players and dropping the match into his giant, yellow frisbee ashtray.

"Such a great day" says my father looking out at the front garden in full, voluptuous bloom. It's midsummer. "You know me and Ma will be going to France beginning of August, yeah?"

'Yeah Dad, I know. I can look after the place when you're away. Don't worry. Me and Marc won't be having any crazy parties, or whatever.'

"I know" he says in an amused way "D'you think we didn't notice all those missing crates of bloody expensive French Burgundy?"

'What!' I say 'What d'you mean, Dad!'

"Oh *come on*!" he responds almost giggling "That disastrous party you and Sam had when you were about 13? 14? We pretended we didn't realise. But *hell*, man! Half the furniture in the house was stuck together with Evostick. When Ma tried to clean the walls it took forever to work out what the hell it was that you had plastered all over them...."

'Not me, Dad!' I find myself 'fessing up 'I didn't chuck eggs all over your study wall! I wouldn't do that!'

"So it was *eggs!*" he says still smiling "Hey it's ok. We always wondered what that gooey substance was. We forgave you years ago. Our wayward offspring! Bloody hell. .. It could have been so much worse. At least you're not a junkie or pregnant at 14 or whatever. Or fallen in love with a dope dealer." *(He seems to have forgotten Conrad.)*

'No Dad, for Christ sake! Have you seriously no trust in me whatsoever?'

"Well, yes. Actually we have a *lot* of trust in you. Me and Mum wanted to talk to you about India."

'Oh, okay then......' I say a little surprised.

"We've noticed it coming up in conversation quite a lot recently. We've been thinking if you really want to go.... I mean, do the serious travelling thing as well..?"

'Yes, what are you getting at Dad?'

"We'll support you. I mean we want you to be safe, not take chances. 18 is a bit young to be doing that kind of travelling - but (he takes a long pause here and takes a drag on his cigarette) Marc is pretty together and responsible, we realise that. We just want you to know that we're here if you need us - that is, if you decide to go, of course. If you run out of money, have any difficulties. That sort of thing....."

I smile and hug him resting my head on his shoulder.

"So then, you going to be meeting up with Marc, you know, flying out there in the Autumn?"

'That's the plan so far....Delhi in November.' I say, and as I do it becomes a reality for the first time in my own mind. I know there and then that I'll be on that flight.

"And I have good friends, colleagues - shrinks, but pretty cool people" he adds "Who have a place just south of Delhi. You might want to look them up ....."

'Really Dad? Could I?' I say genuinely trusting that yes, they would be supportive, my parents.

"Let's talk about it nearer the time" he says, and then reminds me as if I needed it "Not long 'til Marc heads off now?"

'Yeah, he'll probably be going late August, just around the time you get back from St. Pierre actually.'

"Gonna miss him?" My father says knowing the answer already.

'Course Dad, what d'you think?'

My father ruffles my already ruffled hair "You'll be fine, Diabolical. Just fine."

Then as I'm about to wander off towards the kitchen he says:

"Just one more thing I wanted to tell you..."

'Yeah? What's that?'

"You remember Dr Beaufort?"

'Of course I remember Dr Beaufort! Dr B's the only shrink you ever sent me to that I actually liked! My one and only shrink success story as far as I'm concerned.....'

My father looks at me in a warm, but at the same time, serious way and puts his hand on my shoulder. "I hate having to tell you this but Dr Beaufort...... he died recently. I know he helped you a lot at a difficult time. He was ill for quite a while....."

'Oh!' I say, truly shocked, understanding finally why I was never given an explanation when I wanted to go back to him, and for some unknown reason, couldn't. 'Oh poor, poor Dr B....... Shit, that's just the pits! He wasn't even old or anything.......'

"I'm *really* sorry. He was a lovely guy, Dr B, really terrific person and so great with you, wasn't he?"

'Yeah Dad, I know, I know.....'

I go upstairs, sit on my bed and pick up the guitar thinking, feeling, *oh shit, not lovely Dr B.....*

- - - - - - - - - - - - - -

```
Hello Kit
I feel I need to apologise to you. I might have
been a little envious of Dr B and perhaps a tad
critical in my words about him. That wasn't
professional nor was it kind of me. I am truly
sorry he passed away.

Yours remorsefully, Dr M

PS please can you address me from now on by my
first name - Sebastian. I think we can drop the
formalities now. Feeling sad on your behalf :(
```

Part Three

_____

What Happened Next

Letters from the India Trip

December 1972 Hardwar

Dear Mum & Dad

It was so great to speak to you when I got to Delhi. Sorry we couldn't talk longer - the line was awful. So you know I survived the plane! It was quite some flight for a novice air traveller but cool to be in the company of other meditators. I hated the freaking landing though.

Can't remember if I told you but when I met Marc I hardly recognised him. He'd had all his lovely dark Jesus hair cut off (really badly cut too!) - beard gone as well. I'd never actually seen his face before! It was weird! Not his face, but not having ever actually seen it. Like meeting this tall dark stranger for the very first time.

Anyway the Delhi festival was just great (huge actually, people walked for days to get here from their villages) and then we travelled in this ancient, decrepit 1950's bus to Hardwar. It had all these gods and goddesses painted on it. To bless the journey, we thought, which definitely needed blessing! My backside and various other parts of my anatomy ached for days afterwards. We drove for about 5 hours going north from Delhi on the most basic rudimentary dusty and bumpy roads. Hardwar is on the Ganges (you probably know that, but I didn't) and where the main ashram is. That's where I'm writing to you from now. I hope this letter doesn't take months to get to you because we're in the middle of nowhere. Really there's just the few westerners like us who stayed behind to travel (because most people have flown back home now) and the people who work and do service at the ashram. And the only others around seem to be sadhus, religious men, wandering along the river in orange robes and straggly beards looking emaciated. Actually maybe I'll hang onto this letter and post it from Delhi because that's where we're heading back to in a day or two.

I did get a bit ill for a while. There was a pleuritis bug going round all the westerners that everyone seemed to catch and I got it too (of course!). It was really painful to breath, like daggers, but I'm 100% better now. I must have been a bit delirious because at one point I was in the main hall here but I was convinced I was in a railway station waiting for the next train. It never came - the train, that is! I think I scared Marc, but all is well now so don't worry. On the upside so far I've avoided all the stomach bugs that everyone seems to get. That's possibly because the only liquid I trust is bottled ie Fanta and Coca Cola. My stomach's fine but my teeth will probably disintegrate and fall out instead. So book that dentist's appointment for when I get back!

In a few days we're going to get on the road - back down to Delhi and then further south into Rajasthan where Marc's got contact details for these Peace Corps guys. That will take us into proper rural India. Not the usual plasticky tourist places.

I've noticed that people either love or hate being here. Some of them are desperate, crazy even, to get home asap and others are in love with the place. Confronting seeing the levels of poverty that you don't see in Europe. Also quite badly deformed children begging in the street - bit of an eye opener. And we get stared at a lot. I mean A Lot. I haven't worked out yet what that's about. It's not just that we're white westerners - it's much more loaded than that. I'll let you know when I'm any the wiser!

One other thing. I'm wearing a sari! And it hasn't fallen off! Amazing! Those sari wearing instructions Gita went through with me have really paid off. Not sure if I can handle wearing a sari and carrying a rucksack all at the same time though. Too many possible catastrophes and embarrassments - just might be a step too far.

Anyway, I'll keep it shortish and write to you again soon from the next Poste Restante, probably Jaipur. Say a big hi to Jake from me and Sam too if he's around. I miss you all so much - you seem so far away. So til my next instalment.... Love to all

PS You'll never guess what? I've stopped smoking! We can't smoke in the ashram so I've just had to quit (for now). And anyway couldn't smoke when I was ill. So there's the upside.

Late January 1973, Jaipur

Dear Mum & Dad,

We just got to Jaipur this morning and so I can hopefully find somewhere to post this. Would have written earlier but we've been staying in a tiny Rajasthani village about 20 miles from here for the last month. We found the Peace Corp guy who introduced us to a school teacher in the village. And we've (that is Marc, me and a couple of others, musicians actually) been staying there.

It's really primitive. I mean there are no toilets! None. You're probably wondering how on earth people manage with no loos? Well, there are designated fields where you do it. One for men and another for women. And lots of pigs around. It's worse than disgusting! Use your imagination! We called them toilet pigs. Yukk. Problem is we were followed everywhere we went, mainly by curious kids, so ended up creeping to the field under the cover of darkness. Can you believe it! It's enough to give you a serious bowel disorder having to hang on until night fall. Actually, I found somewhere else to go secretly but I'm not really supposed to tell anyone. I don't think you'd grass me up from afar though, would you?

Anyway, the Peace Corps guy has been posted there to help increase their milk yield. The village being in a rare fertile valley with unusually beautiful grazing land - loads of healthy looking cows and water buffalo. I'd say 95% of the villagers have never been as far as Jaipur. So never seen a town of any size or description. No need.

The main deity or god they worship in this particular village is Kali. The Goddess of Wrath. She's pretty terrifying and has this gruesome necklace of bloodied skulls in all the pictures. A couple of days ago when it was very stormy weather we could hear drums beating and people chanting through the night. It was super spooky. Our friend, Krishnan, the school teacher, explained because we were perplexed, that it was to keep the wrath of Kali at bay which they experience as hail for example. Anything that could damage the crops or upset the animals.

The other thing I discovered is that we, us ignorant western idiots, keep offending people with our lack of regard for the customs. Like it's not ok for me to walk around alone with Marc when we're not married. I had no idea. And it's not ok for me to wear my hair loose in public. The other thing that's also not ok, is to wear one ankle bracelet only. It's a sign of prostitution! Who would have known? I was out walking around the village and the women by the well collecting water sort of chucked it at me. I don't mean bucket loads of it, just a sprinkling and they were laughing. I think it was meant to purify me of my evil ways.

Should let you know, before we got here we went to scout out Gita's people in the southern bit of Delhi. It took forever to find them way out in a suburb on the far side of the city. When we eventually got there we discovered they were actually all in mourning. Two family members had just died. Our timing couldn't have been worse! So we ended up 'camping' (minus tent) overnight in a cold, muddy field. In the morning these kind people living in a tiny little corrugated iron shack invited us in for breakfast. They had about 8 kids sleeping in just one room - but they were so generous despite having absolutely nothing apart from a pan of chai and a few chapatis. It made me want to weep.

Marc is keeping a travel diary - so if I forget anything important to tell you he'll have written it down. Next stop is Udaipur - the lake palaces - and then on to Bombay. Might try and do a reverse charge phone call before then. Hope everyone is doing fine. I can hardly remember what it's like back home. It's another world completely. Feels like that anyway.

Lots of love and miss you all v. v. much - even Sam & Jake (but don't tell them!)

February 1973, Goa

Dear Mum & Dad

Thanks a million for posting the money. It will really save our lives out here.

Amazing how very little will go a hell of a long way. Been trying to live on about £1 a day - between the two of us - almost possible if extremely careful. Eating dirt cheap 10 rupee meals, staying over in government hostels or with whoever will put us up (or rather put up with us!). We've tried to get around by hitching too but no one seems to recognise what we're doing. So we ended up literally flagging down these passing lorries. Waving frantically like lunatics. They thought we were nuts. In the end it was easier to go by train. But not that easy!!

We made this impossibly long journey down south from Udaipur heading for Bombay. About 14 hours non-stop. There were chickens and various animals sharing our carriage and no empty seats. People squatting in every available inch of space. So we slept in the luggage racks. The toilets were disgusting and overflowing. Tried desperately to avoid, sweated it out! People who couldn't squash themselves into the train just hung onto the outside of it! For hours! There were more people clinging on outside than there were inside. Probably bodies strewn along the railway track too but didn't want to look too closely.

Bombay was something else! No one told us about the bloody mosquitos! Didn't hang around - got a boat down overnight to Goa where we are right now. In fact, I'm sitting under a palm tree on the beach as I write this. Everyone told us how brilliant and fantastic Goa is, that we'd have a great and cool time here, but something doesn't sit easy with me.

We've spent nearly 4 months adjusting to being in a primarily Hindu country and suddenly we're in Christian Goa. It feels all wrong. Over run by annoying westerners (like us too, of course) but some people have been stuck out here with their big drug habit for years. It has a seedy, desperate feeling about it - outwardly an idyllic Paradise, all beaches and juice bars, but just below the surface you get the dark, creepy underbelly feel. Don't worry I'm in no danger of going off the rails, quite the opposite. And there's something about being flung back into western culture suddenly. I'm not ready! After all this adjustment - I want the real India back. Had a freaky food experience here!

After eating purely veg diet for ages decided to try the fish in Goa, because obviously it has a fishing port too. Fish everywhere. But this particular dish was the hottest thing on planet Earth. Hottest in my entire life. Thought I'd burnt off the roof of my mouth - was impossible to make out what we were eating - could have been old tyres, anything. Drank gallons of water to alleviate the burning - didn't help at all. Marc says it's our Karma for devouring a defenceless living creature.

Yesterday morning on the beach saw a guy standing doing these slow, strangely controlled movements. Like a dance but in slow motion minus a partner. Beautiful but odd. Said to Marc has he gone off the rails - lost the plot? Dropped too much acid maybe?

But turned out he was doing 'Tai Chi' whatever that is? Not so crazy after all. Am learning something new everyday.

Next stop Ellora and Ajanta and then heading east for Benares. Decided to start the homeward journey after that, but not in any great hurry. Will be going back overland with Marc after all. Thought about flying but decided not to. We've been speaking to plenty of travellers, getting the low down and a few contacts, so have pretty realistic idea how to make the trip back safe. Will update you soon as we know more.

Really so great to get your letters. Amazing feeling to turn up somewhere new and find a letter waiting there. Good old Poste Restante! I miss home so much but at the same time can't imagine it any more. Or my life before this. Everything being so super intense out here no brain space left for anything else.

Lots of love to all, human and animal, from your out there daughter.....

March 1973, Amritsar

Dear All (that's Jake and Sam too)

So much happened since I last wrote. Will try and cram it into one airmail letter - if not you'll get part one followed by part two. No, I'm not going to take any unnecessary risks! I'm not completely mad. Stop worrying! We're not intending to hang around with hill bandits whilst crossing the Khyber Pass. It's been done before and will be again! Thousands do it every year. Jeez! Anyway, we won't be crossing the Khyber just yet, so cool down!

Meanwhile, travelled to Ellora and Ajanta. Slept in cave up in the hills. Was terrified of local legendary panther that might stalk us out and gobble us up in the middle of the night. (Far more scary than hill bandits.) Panther didn't show up, instead lovely elderly man from local village did with bowls of dhal and rice. I'll never get over the kindness of people here. People who have nothing. Went to stunning Buddhist temples carved out of the mountainside. These rocky Buddhas even though made of rock look as if they really are breathing. Then went to Khajaraho - all sorts of intricate tantric looking sexual carvings on the outer walls. Bloody hell! Thousands of them all in layers/strata reaching up to the top of the temples. Temples dripping with them. We had a tour guide - he looked shifty as hell trying to explain what it was all about to cynical western people who immediately assume it's simply pornographic. Freudian take on all of this?

(Dad you must have some kind of psycho hypothesis / explanation surely!! Now's your chance, go for it!)

Next stop was Benares. Oh my god! First time I've seen a dead body being burnt. All happening down by the banks of the Ganges. In huge pyres - but all sorts of life going on around. Like the most normal thing in the world to just stumble upon a body or two on your evening stroll. I had nightmares - not quite night terrors but close. Meanwhile people are bathing in the river whilst the disintegrating corpses float past, marigold wreaths chucked in the water, women doing laundry, kids splashing. Sharing our hotel with families of giant rats. I mean Giant. The biggest you've ever seen. I could hear them scuttling about at night, scratching through our rucksacks and belongings. Chewing up the corners of our maps. Marc slept through all of this, of course. How does he do it?

Then crossed back westwards towards Delhi - another super long train ride plus chickens - but decided to stop over in Agra. Big mistake. Tourist hellhole. Accosted by guys touting for everything imaginable. Got to hotel. Monkeys!! Tribes of them marauding across the rooftops stealing whatever food they can find. Amazing site from afar but scary close up. Quite vicious and they spread rabies apparently. Some were carrying their babies. Came all the way over to where we were sitting on roof at sunset. Luckily not in possession of any tasty food items.

Did the Taj Mahal of course, like all the good, boring straight tourists round here. It's just like it looks in the brochures. Pristine, glowing but not sure worth the hassle. Agra is the most disappointing India experience so far.

Got back to Delhi for one last time on board, wait for it, a super modern train! The only one in the entire sub continent, I think. Nothing remotely like the ancient machines we went south in.

Then ended up in New Delhi at Mrs Dunkley's Dog House. It's a B & B (though it has neither beds nor breakfasts) more a dosshouse and not actually called that (Mrs D's Dog House) but it's the most apt description I can come up with. Mrs D herself is Anglo Indian lady with startling psychiatric problems and yes, dogs. She sees things, hears things that no one else does yet **doesn't see what everyone else can**. Right under her nose. Such as her dogs peeing on her guests' sleeping bags.

The place has a notorious reputation as a junkie hang out. Which it is. Guys cleaning their syringes at the well in the yard where you go to wash first thing in the morning, which doesn't appear to bother Mrs D one iota. Lots of people on methadone apparently are stranded in India and can't get home. They mostly seem to be French. Why, I don't know? I will never, I mean Never go back to that dump again. An absolute last resort as we couldn't find anywhere else for a couple of nights before heading north. It's location, bang smack in the middle of New Delhi, is the one and only positive thing about it.

We survived Mrs D and now I'm writing from Amritsar - from a totally different type of guesthouse attached to the Golden Temple. Another world altogether. From the ridiculous to the sublime. Went to the Temple this morning for a 'service' of some sort. Stunningly beautiful place - out of this world surrounded by still lake water and walkways. Mists rising spookily at dawn and behind it super surreal goldenness of the temple across the lake. Removed shoes, was ushered towards plush visitors area, sank into softest carpet ever, witnessed the unwrapping of the holy book swathed and tied in layers of silk. Prayers and chanting, sort of. Interiors painted in subtle and delicate colours and symbols, maybe? Or writing? Couldn't tell, didn't matter. Understood almost nothing - felt brilliant. Could have stayed for months.

At this guesthouse a little boy of about 9 is looking after us, assigned to us it seems, gets us chai and lovely chapati and even special barfi (Indian sweet made from buffalo milk and cardamon seed). Sad because we know we can't stay long. Need to get moving towards the problematic Pakistani border which is only open on a Thursday. Why? It could be something to do with the war, it has been suggested (Oops, maybe shouldn't have written that bit, but too late!)

So there you are. A big catch up. And here we are just outside the Golden Temple. I wish I could magically transport you here.

Not sure when I'll get to write again as we'll will be on the road (Yes! The actual road) from now on but will try and send you an itinerary of Our Plan.

Loads of love to all

8 Weeks later: May 1973, Basel

Dear Estelle

We've finally, yes **finally**, made it to Switzerland as you can see from the post mark! Now kind of taking stock before heading home. Thought I'd write to you before I get back to London in a week or so just to give you the low down. I'll be coming back ahead of Marc because, bloody hell, I don't know why I agreed to this, but it's Jake's barmitsvah and they want me back for it. It's the last thing on earth I can imagine attending. Jeez! I've been dispatching letters home on and off but I can never tell them half of what's actually been going on. They've been getting the sanitised version. So Estelle, I'm giving you the **real story** ahead of our return but please don't let on.

The trip has been an education in the good old university of life sense, an eye opener - at times beautiful and sometimes unbelievably confronting - which I'll fill you in on when back home. But there's other stuff that's been happening that I have to talk to you about - 'near death experiences' - I think that's what I'd call them, that have come in all sizes and shapes. (A bit dramatic sounding I know, but only a slight exaggeration.)

Firstly, I didn't exactly tell the entire truth to the folk back home about getting ill. I actually had pneumonia in the ashram in Hardwar. I was so sick I was beyond caring what happened to me. That's a first! I've put it down - getting so ill, that is - to the massive culture shock. I couldn't cope so my body just shut down. Then I didn't have to. I was delirious, hallucinating and out of my mind for weeks. I vaguely remember someone trying to help me sit up in bed. I certainly couldn't stand or walk, eat or even drink apart from a sip or two. Marc genuinely thought I was dying. It was only after I came through the worst of the delirium that someone got hold of a local doctor who eventually diagnosed it. All across the middle east and the entire journey home my hair has been falling out in bundles. I mean seriously falling out as a result of this illness. I'm not bald but I've lost over half the hair I started out with! So travelling after this illness was hard and losing probably my best attribute in handfuls was even harder.

When we left the Ashram in Hardwar I could barely lift my rucksack off the ground and soon after became manic about food. Went to bed most nights dreaming of breakfast! After breakfast fantasised endlessly about the mouth watering lunch I was going to have and so on like it was the only thing on earth that mattered. I guess my body needed nourishment that badly and it seems to have thrived on the amazing street food on offer everywhere. Marc said I looked like a small neurotic bird when I ate - not exactly an alluring image. I'd lost about 2 stone in those couple of weeks of illness and became a walking advert for safety pins, but on the up side discovered incidentally that I possess amazing cheekbones and deep sunken eye sockets. Quite sexy in a sick, emaciated way.

Thing was, in India I'd always felt relatively safe, but the moment we hit Pakistan it was a different story altogether. Suddenly we both felt exposed, vulnerable and afraid of everything. We hot footed it through Pakistan as fast as humanly possible. It took us about 3 days. There were political riots and unrest in the bigger cities - in Rawalpindi in particular, with army parades and this heavy duty military presence - soldiers, tanks, the whole show. We had no idea what was going on - just aware of perpetual menace. You could taste it in the air, especially after dark. I covered up my hair as much as I could (it being fair) and hid my face. Marc felt it too - the constant threat. The nights were the worst - it was nearly impossible to sleep.

Contrary to all the gory horror stories you've probably heard, Afghanistan turned out to be stunningly peaceful and harmonious after the violence of Pakistan. A massive welcome relief. We travelled south from Kabul to Kandahar and then on to Herat. Actually outside the towns it consists mainly of deserts and villages made of the same sandy mud coloured stone. So the villages rise up and out of the earth and from a distance you can hardly decipher the houses and streets because they're camouflaged. But actually they're teeming with people and animals, markets and noise. Women totally covered in these dalek shaped costumes in shimmering satin-like colours, such as turquoise and purple, that completely engulf them from head to toe with the exception of a tiny rectangle gauze that they can just about see out of. Not sure how they actually breathe or how come they don't keel over with heat exhaustion. It's totally bizarre - never knew anything about this. I mean I get covering your head but your whole body and face? But such lovely hospitable people.

We stumbled across the strongest dope in the known universe in Kabul. Seriously. The joy of getting here got us in the mood for some kind of hedonistic celebration (that's what we told ourselves!) It was not a good experience, probably made worse because neither of us had been smoking. Guess what? I got the night terror thing back - not when under the influence but the next day. Full scale existential melt down of massive proportions: Overnight everything became meaningless. I mean meditation, anything spiritual, anything at all I held dear - people, places, you name it. I found myself making up a story in my head that all the beloved spiritual teachers alive in the world today plus all those who'd gone before them, were simply compassionate, altruistic people who wanted to alleviate the suffering of others by pretending, yes pretending, there was something beyond this physical corporeal existence. All a big fat con. It left me reeling from the hopelessness, the nihilistic void and next thing the freaky childhood angsts came roaring back in like a gigantic wave, a _tsunami of dread._ If my parents get wind of any of this you can bet your life I'll be back in the bloody consulting room before I've made it through passport control. Which is why I'm asking you not to tell anyone. I especially wish I could tell my father that...

Time's up in Shrinksville!

If there are two things I'm never doing again the first is go to another miserable shrink and the other is smoke dope. If you see a joint being passed in my direction snatch it away from me please !! Promise me that, Estelle!! And for god's sake make sure I keep my resolve the next time my dear crazy Dad suggests I need some fucking _'help'_ !

Ok, back to the travelling: Leaving Afghanistan and crossing into Iran was another kind of near death experience. Well, sort of. We'd picked up a ride in an ancient jeep with a neurotic English guy, two laid back German guys and a really cool, lovely American girl. In the end the six of us rode together for about 4 weeks until we got to Istanbul which is a hell of a long journey. Have a look on the map if you get a moment. We all swore we wouldn't take any dope across any of the borders as it was too risky and none of us had any idea what the penalties might be. Some places out here actually imprison and execute you (so I'd been told) but we didn't know which were the worst or most notorious border crossings. But on the Afghani/Iranian side guess what? Freddie and Johnny - the German guys - got busted (they'd concealed their stash in various hidden pockets inside their shoulder bags) which meant we all got detained for hours. The jeep was virtually taken apart piece by piece. It was held together with bits of string and wire and gaffa tape in the first place, so that really did it no favours in terms of roadworthiness.

Some of these border guards, seriously, couldn't have been more than 12 or 13 years old and were over the moon, ecstatic with their 'find'. Next they started skinning up and smoking it whilst interrogating us in indecipherable English. We had absolutely no idea what our fate might be in the hands of these kids. Estelle, they had guns too. But thank god, they confiscated the remaining stash - the stuff they hadn't got around to smoking yet and eventually let us go free. Marc was white with apoplectic rage at Johnny and Freddie for being so insanely reckless and endangering all of us. That they would put us all at risk after assuring us they were squeaky clean. Marc's explosive fury though was something else, never seen it in action before; now Johnny and Freddie can't do enough to appease him. They're virtually grovelling like slaves at his feet.

Oh and I forgot, I had a pregnancy scare - no period for about 8 weeks - but I came on, of course, whilst we were being detained at this border. I sat on this rusty bucket in a broken down wooden shack with no proper door, bleeding profusely whilst shitting myself with fear. Not a pretty sight.

Moving onto near death experience number three. Simon, the owner of the jeep, turned out to be one of those angsty, nervy guys with a full-on control problem. Your quintessential control freak. He would not, simply could not, let anyone else drive. There were six of us. Three (including Simon of course) would sit up in the front and the remaining three had just about enough room to grab some sleep in the back since we were on the road pretty much day and night. This guy, Simon, just insisted on driving even when he was falling asleep at the wheel. No one apart from me, that is, seemed to realise what was going on because they were all either stoned or unconscious. They do not realise how many times I kept that bloody idiot awake when he was about to take us over the edge. I dared not sleep. Sleep equalled death as far as I was concerned. Sleep was not my friend. I felt it was my duty to stay awake. I cannot count the number of times I rammed my elbow into Simon's ribs and yanked at his annoying greasy hair to keep us all in the land of the living.

Simon had never been further east than the Pakistani border with India. He spent his days going back and forth between Istanbul and Pakistan stopping off periodically in this suburb of Tehran with university professor/lecturer friends.

It was with them that I discovered the extent of my hair loss. We hadn't washed or showered for about 2 weeks. When I stepped out of their (western style, utterly luxurious) bathroom (plus proper sit down loo with flush) I was carrying half my hair in my arms. Felt great to be cleansed of several weeks' worth of dirt and sweat but lousy of course to be half bald. They then organised an appointment with a hair specialist in Tehran (who incidentally was completely bereft of any hair of his own therefore not instilling that much confidence). He put the loss down to my illness a few months earlier in Hardwar. Up til that point I hadn't realised that's what happens when you get seriously ill.

I really liked this Iranian couple though - the university people. They helped us get to grips a bit with the politics - life under the Shah; they were hanging in there hoping for a revolution that would make a difference especially for these millions of really poor people in rural Iran. That's what they said they were holding out for. The split was huge. It was impossible to ignore the American influence. It was everywhere. The roads, for example: the moment we entered Iran we sort of slid and swerved onto these beautifully tarmacked, smooth, silent roads (paid for with the dollar). To be honest Estelle, they made us nauseous after the crummy pot-holed tracks we'd driven down all these countless miles.

I have a confession to make now. Nobody knows this, so don't tell a soul. I had a mad, bad, heartbreaking crush on Freddie. Freddie has this waist length red henna hair, large slightly sad amber coloured eyes and a warm, insanely funny personality. A kind of hennaed Gypsy guy. He's been Johnny's minder of sorts on the entire journey out of India all the way home. I mean Johnny is a full blown junkie - a walking, emaciated shadow - dark sunken eyes, yellowish skin. I think Freddie was trying to get him home to Frankfurt in one piece. No easy task. A serious substance abuse casualty is Johnny - Marc thinks he's a heroin addict. That didn't stop Cara (the American girl travelling with us) from kind of falling for him just like I was falling for Freddie, I suppose. But Estelle, honestly it was almost unbearable being physically so close to Freddie but unable to do anything about it. I was going out of my mind (and body). Trying endlessly to concoct a bunch of implausible reasons to hang out alone with him and naturally feeling guilty as hell. I had my 19th birthday in Istanbul and Freddie was, how can I put it, very attentive in an innocent sort of way. When we all parted a few days later I felt unbelievably bereft. In fact the last time I saw Freddie we were shunting Simon's clapped out jeep back onto the ferry. Marc didn't seem to notice anything strange about my behaviour and I have no idea if Freddie cottoned on how intense my feelings were. Even if he had done Marc's wrath was a force of nature so I doubt he'd have laid a finger on me. Jeez. I'm a bad, bad person.

The last truly stupid thing I did was in Thessalonika. We were on the home stretch (but not quite able to ease up on the budget) when we discovered we could sell our blood in the local hospital. Yes, really. It's what hard up travellers often do. Marc has O negative and my god, Estelle, they were all over him like starving, rampant vampires. They wanted his blood like it was the rarest commodity on Earth. It turned out I have boring old A and low blood pressure as well (traveller's curse apparently). They almost couldn't be arsed to collect mine because it was going to take a while to extract it from my sluggish veins and they probably had vats of the stuff hanging around in their labs. But they did in the end and of course Marc's was harvested before he'd even decided he actually wanted to give it up. But here's the stupid bit. We were all over the place after this, feeling a bit faint and extremely hungry with nowhere to crash for the night. (And secretly I was missing Freddie too which didn't help the mood.) Anyway we ate pineapple rings out of a tin sitting on a bench at the train station and proceeded to spend our blood money getting smashed all night on cheap Retsina. I don't think I've ever felt as shite as I did by the next morning. Felt like dehydrated, anaemic half life and filthy too but cannot honestly call this near death experience number four (despite feeling like death warmed up). Not really.

When I get home Estelle, my parents are going to notice firstly my hair and then they'll see I have a fair number of sores that just haven't healed, particularly one massive mosquito bite on my back I've had since Bombay that's gone septic. I don't know why I haven't been able to heal these small things. Maybe because of the pneumonia and being run down? Maybe because I've been living on oranges, yoghurt and flatbread for the last few months?

Being bloody doctors, they'll surely send me straight to the Hospital for Tropical Diseases before you can blink.

Anyway, I've decided I'm going to make sure I wear my most flamboyant/outrageous Sari to Jake's barmitzvah. No. In fact that will be the one condition of my attendance! I have no idea why he's putting himself through it. He can't stand all that ritualistic stuff. It'll be the second time only in my entire life that I've set foot in a synagogue; you remember when Sam had to do the same? My parents insist it has to happen 'for the grandparents' sake. Sam always insisted he did it for the money.

I'm absolutely dreading the whole crazy shebang but I promised I'd be there, so I will. In fact we made a concerted effort to drag ourselves back to Europe so I could get home in time for this. Maybe you can come too? Wear your famous holey dirndl skirt with the burn marks all over it! Testament to our misspent youth! We could both go barefoot! A barefoot revolution!

So just to let you know the timing I'll be getting a train from Switzerland the week after next, probably Tuesday or Wednesday? Marc's going to stay on for a bit. Really I'm here just trying to acclimatise - hang out with Marc's friends, eat rosti, get myself together before having to face coming home. Hope I haven't freaked you out so far with my scary tales but thanks a million for being there Estelle. What would I do without you? Feels so good to tell you all this and get it off my chest. Can't wait to see you again and properly catch up!

Lots of love

Kit

Ps Hope your parents haven't been giving you too much hassle? No more ghastly Italian finishing schools or whatever?

10 Years Later

London

Spring 1983 - Back to Shrinksville with Dr Shenley (a potential new female analyst) - the first one I've ever voluntarily chosen to see.

When I was younger it used to amaze me
that people just wandered around
completely undaunted
not ghostly and haunted
like me - but then I was the one who was crazy

Hi, yes, hello is that Dr. Shenley? Umm........ my father, he's a shrink, I mean psychoanalyst too, he's recommended I come and see you. I'm not living in London all of the time - I'm sort of commuting between London and Cornwall.... but I want to come back to London for good, soon that is..... as soon as I can. Ok, so it's alright if I see you when I'm in town? That's great. Yes, I can do next Wednesday. Oh, just one other thing - if I can't get a baby sitter can I bring my son? He's just a baby - he'll be one in July.

Wednesday, May 1983 - First Session with Dr Shenley

Why am I here?

That's a big question..... The main thing is I got *Globus*.... you know, *Globus Hystericus.* For the last nine months or so since I had my baby, Evan, I thought I was going to suffocate. Then I thought I was going mad. I had this permanent feeling of an enormous lump in my throat. I'd go to bed at night afraid that I'd be dead by the morning. I've been driving the local GP in the village nuts with my multiple visits. My parents just sent me to an ENT guy in Harley Street who told me the whole thing has been brought on by anxiety and that I'd probably start noticing the symptoms disappear if I felt 'reassured'. Can you believe it? It's exactly what's beginning to happen. Thank God.

How come I've been so anxious?

I had a baby as you know ..... well I had a baby with a guy I'd only known for 4 weeks. I met him through Citizen Band radio. Yeah, I know it sounds all very truckers and American. People use CB radio here too, you know - there's a kind of pirate community. I'm always attracted to non-mainstream things. Wacky, rebellious things, so I naturally got attracted to it and met Evan's dad that way. He wanted me to have a termination. Absolutely no way! The minute I found out I was pregnant I felt completely and utterly protective of this baby. I'd never felt the biology kick in like that. Zero maternal instinct one moment, the fiercest, deepest connection the next.

His dad?

Well, his dad was in a bit of trouble. He'd been busted not so long before we met. He was sort of, well, umm, how can I put it..... an international drug smuggler. And of course he was estranged from his family. Or maybe his dear wifey tipped them, Customs and Excise or whoever, off. No one's letting on. Anyway, to cut a long story short: When I met him he was due up in court in a few months and had been told by his solicitor that he was likely to go to prison for about 5 years. He used all the terminology like "*I'll be going down for 5 years - that is if I can't prove that what I had on me was me 'personal'*" ie not stuff he was selling, dealing, you know. It sounded like something from the telly. I was pregnant almost immediately and he, well, asked me to promise, that I wouldn't tell anyone until after the court case. That is, after he realised there was no way I'd have a termination. I always wondered why he wanted it kept secret but I think he was hoping for a reconciliation with the wife still.

So I pretended, because I was living back at home, all through this vile morning sickness and weird symptoms that I was just, well, a bit depressed. I could hardly move an inch without wanting to throw up. But I kept up the act for a while. My body language was totally odd and stilted. My parents must have thought I was having a breakdown or something or becoming bulimic. Whilst this whole charade was going on I was apply for jobs and going to interviews with the pretext of looking for work. I'd actually show up and do the interview as if I genuinely wanted the job and then get disappointed if I didn't get it. That made me feel a bit crazy. A bit schizophrenic.

Then just before that Christmas - it was now only a few weeks until the court case - but I just couldn't keep a lid on it. I went for a walk with my mother on the Heath and she was so worried about me. I really felt for her and wanted so badly to tell her. She eventually, actually said the standard line '**You aren't pregnant are you?**' Of course, that was my opportunity to come clean and I said yes, I am. I was about 4 months gone then. She was so supportive and seemed absolutely relieved. In other words, I wasn't going off the rails, I was just 'plain, simple, ordinary *pregnant*'.

What's that got to do with why I'm anxious now?

Well, at first things turned out better than we thought. His court case came up in the new year and he got a suspended sentence, miraculously. No one could believe it, least of all him. So he invited me to go with him to Cornwall. He'd bought this enormous converted coach, painted black with a gigantic silver guitar on the side of it. In a former life it had been used for motor racing meetings - it could carry a car for Christ sake, in the back of it. He'd bought it, incredibly, with the proceeds of his dope dealing which somehow hadn't been confiscated by the courts.

So I went with him to start a new life out in the sticks. I was by then about 6 months pregnant and living on a bus at the back of a container yard because we had to be hidden from view. It's amazing how impossible it is to live a so-called *'free'* life. You can't stop off anywhere without the police hassling you. None of the camp sites would take us because we looked so ostentatious, you know with the gigantic silver guitar and all of that, and we couldn't afford to pay anyway.

I just realise what I'm telling you. We were actually living the traveller life, proper Gypsy life, for a while - on the edge, unwelcome and always about to be moved on..... it was really hard and unsettling.

Eventually my parents bailed us out and bought us a cottage (temporary investment sort of arrangement) in this tiny fishing village almost on the beach, right by the sea wall. My baby, Evan, was three months old when we moved in. But the throat thing, the feeling of suffocation had already started.

Something happened around the time he was born too. I was in the hospital in Devonport surrounded by all these Navy wives, their husbands had been posted to the Falklands. I felt so out of place and not part of their world. And then the birth itself was scary as hell. Just before it, I would look around at people in the street, anyone really, and tell myself *they all got out* (of the womb, that is) so this baby would get out too, somehow. It seemed so utterly impossible.

Then when I saw Evan for the first time, I fell madly in love with him. He was so beautiful and fragile. One night in the hospital I had a sort of waking dream: I looked at my hands and arms and at first I looked like a new born baby myself, my limbs all out of control and entirely new to the world. And then suddenly I was looking at the arms and hands of an ancient, shrivelled up woman on her death bed. It terrified me.

This thin line between life and death. The evaporation of time.

I guess I was just really out of my depth. Lonely, new baby, new place to live. No sense of any kind of security or future. I'm still living there, in the village, most of the time but I'm desperate to come back to London. Be with my family and my friends. Not be so fucking lonely. Have a life. I feel like life is going on here, in London, and I'm not part of it anymore annexed out in the middle of nowhere. That makes me feel unbelievably sad sometimes.

What made me stick it out so far in the west country?

That's a pretty loaded question isn't it? I mean I've been *trying*, trying being the operative word, to make a go of it with Evan's dad. I wasn't just going to bale out and trot off home to mummy and daddy without giving it my all. Yes, it's been an incredible challenge. I'm not a country person, I'd never normally have done this, but then this isn't a 'normal' situation. It never bloody is, with me. I'm sure you must be getting the gist by now?

And anyway, you know the first time we saw the cottage it was a beautiful Indian summer's day. The sea was way out and calm. Flat like Lake bloody Placid. The beach looked huge and peaceful and golden. Then the actual weekend we moved in was on the Autumn equinox and the tide was massively high with the south easterlies blowing gale-force straight at us. I thought the waves would wipe us out. The glass in our windows was visibly bending in the wind and these gigantic rollers smashing into the sea wall at the end of our back yard. I thought that would be it. All over. And now I've started to hate the sound of the wind through our roof tiles. It never lets up. It's so bloody relentless.

It's like all these things that look so great and beautiful but have this shadowy side that you just don't want to see until it's staring you in the face. Like the other day, a little sailing boat got swept up onto the rocks just by our bay. We could see it from our window. One minute it's literally all plain sailing, the next you're shipwrecked and then the mean-spirited villagers are down on the beach grabbing anything useful of yours they can get their thieving hands on. Where's the community spirit in that, then? Can you imagine those poor people watching their belongings firstly getting smashed up and then the remnants being nicked?

You want to know about other relationships? Hmm, you would, I guess?
Well, I was with Marc my first 'proper' boyfriend for 9 years from just before my 17th birthday. We did loads together. When I think

about it now. Bloody hell. We travelled east, we got seriously into meditation (which I still do). If you've got a 'thing' about meditation - if you think it's rubbish then there's no way we can work together. You don't? Really? That's ok then.

Marc and me, we ran a kind of alternative meditation centre for about 2 years after we got back from India. We had our own band and a theatre group. I wrote a lot of songs, other people created plays and sketches which we performed regularly. We lived communally with anywhere between about 9 and 14 or 15 people. My friend Estelle joined us too. That was great. I'm so glad she did. We put on loads of small events at our place with our own music, poetry, theatre kind of thing... We did yoga and meditated for at least an hour every morning. Actually we were incredibly together and super disciplined. I think I'd had to grow up quite fast because after a while I got, what do they say, stir-crazy, wanted to break free, and both he and I had affairs during our relationship. Later on after our commune had ended we lived back at my parents' house in Hampstead for about 5 years. I worked with him, Marc, in the music business too for a while, sound equipment side, long story. It was quite an experience for an introvert like me. Especially when the punk thing happened and all our peaceful, flower power ways were utterly challenged. There was a lot of aggro around. But most important I guess, is that I never felt he, Marc that is, loved me. Maybe he did, in his own way but I just never felt it.

After we split up I ended up in Miami Beach for 6 months working as a chamber maid in these crummy, cockroach infested hotels in the steamy tropical weather minus a green card, which became an issue with my various employers. I sweated it out, literally, and hung around with other meditators that I vaguely knew. One or two who I knew from London. Had some short lived pretty ghastly relationships but nothing worked out. Did some crazy stuff - took a trip from Miami to Columbia at one point with no money. Had to beg to be let back into the USA and was on the verge of being deported. Soon after that I flew back to London courtesy of a forged airline ticket on a BA flight. I had these South American 'friends' who could organise that kind of thing for about a quarter of the actual ticket price. God, that was scary! Meanwhile, and this is the more important bit, Marc had got together with someone else (actually they were already having this scene long before he and I split up) and they had a baby, like, pretty much straight away. Therefore I thought, I assumed, I was infertile - I never got pregnant with Marc though we hadn't use any protection for absolutely years. Ironic, considering the situation I'm now in, don't you think?

What else? What else is bothering me now?

I feel frightened *all* the time. The life/death thing. Either for myself or for Evan. I love him so much. Am always aware of how utterly fragile everything really is especially since the birth. And no one will talk about it. This big secret. We're all scared shitless but no one will admit it. Will they? That is apart from my father who is a massive hypochondriac amongst other things. But even he won't talk openly about his fears - his are all dimmed down with a cocktail of super strength prescription medications.

So yes, the basic reason I'm here is that I feel like everything's hanging by a thread and sometimes, mostly actually, in fact pretty much all the bloody time, I'm on the verge of not being able to cope.

And, I suppose it's obvious - you don't even need to read between the lines. But I'm breaking up with Evan's dad. We don't actually say it out loud but we both know it isn't working out. He's angry and frustrated. He punched a hole in one of our walls just recently. It hurt him more than it did any real damage to the wall. He's been a good dad though. Especially when Evan was first born. He has a daughter who's about 3 or 4 now. He never sees her - I can't imagine that. Must be so painful. But he knows how to be with babies. When he first saw Evan I think he fell in love with him, despite his protestations and not wanting another kid. It's really hard this separation stuff, isn't it. I feel guilty and selfish.

Am I sure it's over?

Yes. I had this 'epiphany' - I think that's what you call it - one day in the cottage when I was hoovering the rush matting. I thought this could be my life from now on. Hoovering the fucking matting and wandering along these pitiful, miserable lanes in the winter pushing a baby buggy. Not a soul about. And living on an absolute shoe-string and under the shadow of his 'suspended sentence'. For the dope dealing, that is. That was when I decided that I had to leave. If I'd felt more loved and secure then it could have been an entirely different scenario.

You know that's been my sole purpose in life (apart from finding a way to live forever, that is). To be loved, to feel safe with someone and it's been an absolute disaster. I never gave a shit about 'achievement', whatever that's supposed to mean, or anything remotely like that. Like I said I just wanted to feel love and to feel safe and I still do. Oh sorry, didn't mean to get so bloody emotional. Can I take one? Tissue, I mean?

This rural idyll stuff is crap too. It's not what it's cracked up to be. It's just horribly lonely and everyone bitches about you. I had these women from the WI knocking on the door one day complaining that I had breast fed in a public place and would I kindly stop doing it with 'immediate effect'? Who the hell do they think they are, those mean-lipped, post menopausal curtain-twitchers! Yes, I know I sound angry, I *am* angry at the pettiness. The narrow-mindedness. But yes, I'm about to become a very single parent.

You want to know about my background? Of course you do!
How long have you got?

Wednesday, April 1985 - My Last Session with Dr Shenley

You keep reminding me this is our last session and that it feels unfinished, somehow. I'm sorry there's been a bit of a gap since I last came, just so much going on right now. I suspect you think I haven't really 'done the work' or whatever you say. Whatever the jargon is. I'm not sure I know what 'doing the work' really means anymore. Seriously though, a hell of a lot has happened since I started seeing you, don't you think? I've properly left Cornwall and Evan's dad now. That's such a huge thing for me. I mean, moving back to London too. That's what I desperately wanted. So that's great. But I didn't realise that joining a Gestalt therapy group meant I couldn't keep coming here. It was a bit of a shock to me, your reaction that is. It was alright me going to a psychic counsellor, you didn't mind that, but not alright me joining this group? But anyway, this Gestalt thing is only temporary. Just wanted to try out a different approach.

When you've been going to shrinks and especially surrounded by Freudian psychoanalysts since the beginning of time you sometimes just want to try out other things, don't you?

Anyway, there's been some incredibly good stuff happening since I saw you a few weeks back. Guess what! .... I got into university! Yup, can you believe it? I've been accepted! I got the letter just yesterday morning. Apparently it doesn't matter that I flunked my education so far, they don't give a shit that I only have a few crappy GCE's - because I qualify as a mature student and they've based their decision on my interviews and their entrance exams plus my portfolio work. Actually, I have a whole new dilemma now but it isn't such a bad one to have. I've been accepted to do both art and music but I can't logistically do both, so I have to make a choice. Pretty great though?

Also, and this is where it gets even better, they have an amazing creche on the campus where Evan can go. It's in beautiful grounds, with lakes, ducks and country trails for the kids to learn about nature, that kind of stuff. I mean he'll be 3 when I start in September which is just the right age - that's what they've told me, anyway. I think he's going to be ok there.

But this age thing is so weird. Like I can't believe that now, at the age of, I mean very nearly 31, I finally, actually, *want* to go to college. I always loathed the idea. Equated it with prison actually. Loss of liberty. Can you believe it? Where was I coming from? And now it fills me with adrenalin but in a freakin' great way. Like my life is starting up all over again.

Something happened when I had Evan, you know. Despite the horrendous anxiety or maybe even because of it, I think all this creativity got unleashed. All those years of pent-up, unspent energy with nowhere to go suddenly has an outlet now. I don't understand it completely. But I hope you can be happy for me too. Would that be an ok thing to want?

Anything else before we finish?

Oh yeah. One more thing I absolutely *have* to tell you before I go. It's a really important development. My dear Ma. You know how seriously ill she'd been a while back? I've been meaning to update you. She's still doing well which means she's been in remission for a quite a bit now, which is a massive relief for all of us, especially for Dad, of course. Actually he's been behaving himself recently too, but that's a whole other thing. But mostly what I wanted to let you know is it's so lovely, so fantastic - watching her, Mum that is, and her relationship with Evan. Her being able to help me and reassure me about being a mother too. I mean, I hadn't a clue. She has this stunning insight, it turns out, about parenting and how kids develop. I genuinely never knew. It's a bit of a bleeding revelation actually. And she's talking to me about it.

Something's changed so dramatically between us. Like a kind of healing, dare I say it even. There's no other way to describe it. I feel her warmth, her being there, like I never ever did when I was a kid myself. You know, because I've told you countless times, I was terrified of her when I was little and we didn't have a warm, close relationship then at all.   And I feared being like her so, so much.

But it's as if this is a completely new person altogether, my Mum and maybe me too? Maybe I'm a new person too in her eyes now. Might that be possible, d'you think?

Ok, I can see you looking at your watch. Is it time?

Thank you, really, I know you tried to help me. I think you did. Just a bit. And I'm not the easiest person in the world to, you know, *'help'*. Resistant as hell! Ambivalent (that's a word you like a lot, I've noticed), unbelievably stubborn too. We've both known that all along, haven't we? But thank you for everything. Better go now before I cry or something.......

Oh just one very last thing.... Now this'll make you laugh. I've been thinking recently of maybe, wait for it, doing a ***psychotherapy training***! Not just yet, I mean I want to live a little first, do my art degree and all of that, but at some point in the future when Evan's just a bit older.

Don't look so bloody surprised! Steady on! You look like you're seriously about to keel over. You've gone all pale and strange. Can I get you a glass of water or something?

Postscript: London, January 2018

- - - - - - - - - - - - - -

Hi Sebastian

I know I haven't been in touch for a while but I really did want to send you the rest of my just completed 'book'. You were sort of responsible for the start of it and it's a curious thing that we never met but I feel like we have. If you read it, you'll be the first.

I know you were worried about me but I'm genuinely doing great. This writing process has been pretty special - so much has come together and I don't quite know how.

Curious thing is I feel like I've sorted out what I needed to, though we never actually got around to setting up that first appointment. And then I heard you retired anyway. Weird, hey?

"The Very Strange and Unlikely Case of Ms Lindfield and Dr Maelstrum".

Thank you & all the very best
Kit x

PS Book No 2 is in the pipe line. It has to be written! I've only got to just over the age of 30 with the first one (and the last part I realise now is far too rushed - there's another book just with that section). So now that you have the time let me know if you fancy proof reading the next one?

- - - - - - - - - - - - - - -

Hi Kit
So good to know you're doing well! I look forward to reading the rest of your book.

I just want to thank you too for putting me in touch with your marvellous therapist colleague. I feel we're doing great work, tackling the relevant issues and for the first time I can imagine taking an extended, much overdue trip overseas. The freedom is beguiling. I feel the road is calling. Costa Rica! Mexico! Who knows! And better late than never, as they say! So I have you to thank for that. *If not for you* (that's a Bob D song isn't it?) I would still be stuck in that stuffy north London practice listening to my patients droning on about ...... well, we won't go there, will we? Please scrub that last sentence.

Cheers!
Sebastian

PS Did I ever mention my younger brother? He was the golden boy, you know the one who could do no wrong in my parents' eyes. He makes me sick to the........ and now, Eureka! I can feel this rage rising through my body like a flow of ferociously hot lava! And my mother ! Cow towing to his every utterance like a grovelling love struck teenager... the complete and utter snivelling.... BITCH!

There I said it at last! I've waited absolutely years to get that off my chest!

PPS by all means please send any writing for proof reading. S x

FIN

_____

Poems, Credits & Acknowledgements

Shrink Rap Generation

It's like this between the patient & the shrink:
one will free associate while the other tries to tell you
what they think that you might think

Who is who, you may well wonder: does it really matter?
One's a little thinner, the other slightly fatter
That's because it's a sedentary profession
All day sitting, sitting, sitting, witnessing confession

So can you really tell, whose world we contemplate?
What's the purpose of this meeting
Little flashes fleeting
Of a less neurotic state?

Hey, just give it to me on a plate!
Or I'll leave you for another,
willing to stand in for my mother, father, brother...

Plenty of them around & strangely, mainly in north London
Mecca of the swallowed back persona, deeply deep in diagnosis
A penny for your thoughts, a pound for your psychosis

And have you ever thought, if you sit and if I lie
You never have to look at me, and meet me eye to eye?

Bit of a cop out really..... considering this is all about relating,
loving, losing, bitter, bruising, bile-releasing hating
Every moment of our time supposedly together -

3 years, twice a week, talking to the ceiling
until you'll stand for it no longer
and ask me in a detached kind of murmer (intended for my healing)

"What are your masturbation fantasies?"

Of course, I now wonder, am I thought of as a wanker
Am I talking bollocks or whatever?
and I reply:

"Well basically, I never.....

have any particular fantasies, I just get into the physical feeling"

But what I really want to say is:
"You're rather like a rapist when it's my dignitiy you're stealing
You penetrate with your Wilkinson's sword intervention
Quite phallic in intention
and destroy this fragile feeling...

I hate you! Are you satisfied now we have at last
surrendered to the roles in which we've both been cast -
A duet of 'negative therapeutic relating'
of countless shrink-wrapped generations
But I don't buy, these formulae
or potted textbook explanations"

It's like this sometimes between the patient & the shrink
If you let somebody tell you what it is, *they* think you think.

Mirror

The first thing you ever said to me was
"So this is how it is for you"
Those words have never left me,
Although you left long ago

Yes "this is how it is"..... such a very simple thing to say
Because no one had ever seen me (or seen through me) in that way

I said, I suppose you're just a mirror
nothing less, nothing more
You said, then shine on crazy mirror
I mean, isn't that what mirrors are for?

Yes, I said, but you'll see all these broken parts of me:
my Inner Cast of Castaways
Gallery of Rogues & Thieves and who believes
any of this stuff anyway?
You'll stumble on my witch
my bitch, my beggarwoman
beggars banqueting, this feast

340

is for the starving and the dispossessed
for my Beauty & my Beast

But that is not the worst of it.... the worst is yet to come
You must have guessed, that I am possessed, by one....

Tiny Little Baby

Before I could go on you said: "We've all got one of those
inside, and anyway who knows
how much worse it would have been, if you hadn't found her now"

I said "but she's so wracked with hunger, emaciated, weak
She hasn't even got a mouth to eat or speak...."

"Shh..." you said... "give her time and treat her like you would
treat any little baby, if you could"

And so I did
That was long ago and if you should ever see her
she will remember, *you* believed her....
And she'll wonder where on earth the time has flown

You'll see she has a mirror and it's a crazy, shiny mirror,
now she holds a mirror of her own

In The Park

I'm leaving, you said in the park, completely out of the blue
When? I said, not really looking at you....
not really wanting to....

Tomorrow, you said, why? Dunno, I said, you lied.
Is there someone else? No. If there was
would you tell me? No, I would not, you replied....

And avoiding all eye contact you were thinking -
Wow, this is easy ! If I go now before she sees me....hesitate,
before she goes hysterical or gets into a state..
Look, you know you'll always be

Special, *very* special to me
There's no one quite like you....
Oh yeah, no one quite as stupid, as trusting, as naïve
I said, or as bloody easy to leave !

It's me, you say, turning ever so slightly away....
It's that dark little corner inside,
that I've always warned you about and you never tried
to find out, did you.....

Didn't I ? This is the first conversation we've had
in years, or am I going mad?
How am I supposed to know anything when you never speak to me....

Oh no, not that old chestnut again... what is it about talking,
communicating
that's so damn sacred....Blah, blah, blah – is that better?
A little conversation, a little appetite whetter?
Ok, here's one for the road – *It's over* – or should I write it all out in a
letter?

And watching us up on this hill we almost look like normal people
having a normal walk & talk in the park.....
Casually you kick a tiny pebble
it misses its target and shoots off into the dark
red night sky, shattering the silence
Like shattering a universe

Hey, look what you did!

Stars start to collapse downwards
followed by chards of glass
and I start to collapse inwards
and like a kid, I'm pulling up handfuls of grass

Suddenly I'm 3 years old and I'm thinking of my dad knowing
there's *nothing* I can do to stop him going

Hey dad, look at me, I can do cartwheels....
hey dad, look at me I can draw pictures...really real ones...
hey dad, I'm very scared of the night..... now I'm screaming...
hey dad, tell me please, it's not really real, say it's just that I'm
dreaming...

Dad? Suddenly I'm 3 years old and it doesn't matter how *bad,* dad, it
gets.....

And then I find myself saying to *you* as if *you* were my dad -
and I feel like I'm shouting but I'm only just whispering

"If it's something I do, I swear I will be different"

And just at that moment, I catch you off guard and I notice you're
not really listening

I Didn't Know

I didn't know, I only guessed, that the fabric could wear so thin

I didn't know, that nothing is certain, or at least
I knew it a long time ago
But I have spent years, waging war on my fears
convincing myself that to show

Such signs of 'weak mind', blind leading the blind
and that those of a likewise condition
will qualify for
a lifetime of poor
self esteem and perpetual suspicion

You see I was right, to be scared of the night
It was never just my paranoia
and if I walk down this road
and the pavements explode
there'll be no point in calling my lawyer

When I was younger, it used to amaze me
that people just wandered around
completely undaunted
not ghostly and haunted
like me - but then I was the one who was crazy

I didn't know, that again I would feel
how fragile the earth that I'm walking

your concrete and steel
your fist and your zeal
It's not the language I'd chose to be talking

But it's all broken down
It's all broken now
into hundreds and thousands of pieces

I will pretend right 'til the end
'til the extinction of every last species

That I didn't know, I only guessed that the fabric could wear so thin

A short piece on some big subjects: Love, Death, Trust and Timing

You told me you'd be there with me

Until the end of my days, you said

So I tried to imagine, me being loved

As I lay there, me, being dead

But now you've changed your mind

It was all made up, so you say

And what did become of your undying love?

I guess it just died an untimely death

Quite sometime before *I* passed away..........

And now that it's over, I go over and over

and over the scenes in my head

How could I ever imagine, me being loved

As I lay there, me, being dead?

All Poems - Kit Lindfield

Acknowledgements

Many dear friends, contemporaries and also comrades from the psychotherapy world have given their support and feedback, listened to my ideas and hung on in there with me as this book has evolved.

I also have to acknowledge the shrinks in whose consulting rooms I spent many a long (50 minute) hour in my earlier life, some of whom I have described in quite uncompromising terms. I know I gave you a pretty rough ride but I learnt from every single encounter and for that I have to give thanks and appreciation.

My son (Evan in the story) has helped in numerous ways, advancing the creative ideas to illustrate the story itself, shaping up the visuals and tackling all the tricky technicalities involved in actually making this happen. And just as my brothers and I experienced when we were growing up, he too had to adapt to a psychotherapy practice encroaching on his home life.

Finally, my long deceased parents came alive to me in this process that I've come to speak of as 'communing with the dead'. I learned that it is never too late to rediscover (or perhaps discover for the very first time) that in the final analysis it is always about love.

Cast of Characters

Family Members:

Kit (me)

Sam (older brother by one year and 11 days)

Jake (younger brother by 6 years)

Marion (mother)

Ezra (father)

Evan (son)

Grandpa Aaron (maternal grandfather)

Rose (maternal deceased grandmother)

Auntie Sara (maternal great aunt)

Granny Fanny (paternal grandmother)

Grandpa Charlie (stone deaf paternal grandfather)

Other Important People:

Candace (dope smoking initiator)

Conrad (corrupter of minors)

Helena (comrade and absconder)

Christa (politically aware au pair)

Marc (my first 'real' longterm boyfriend and lifelong friend)

Estelle (dear friend/rebel whose life has taken a similar course)

Georgina (my oldest childhood, family friend)

Evan's dad (father of my only child)

My Spiritual Master/Teacher (who kept me sane all these years)

The (almost) Silent Stars of the Story, my Shrinks:

At 9: **Fat Ankles** (3 x per week before school for 2 years)

At 13: **Abby** (once a week for a few months after getting arrested)

At 15: **Dr Beaufort** (once a week for 2 or 3 years – the one I liked)

At 17: **Dr Kniffler** (6 weeks – scary, made the Freudians seem mild)

At 29: **Dr Shenley** (2 x week for 3 years, complicated transference relationship)

And of course, a shrink, but never quite *my* shrink, the not so silent **Dr Sebastian Maelstrum**

Song Titles & Quotes

Don't Come Knocking - **Dave Edmunds**

I don't want to achieve immortality through my work; I want to achieve
immortality through not dying - **Woody Allen**

The first cut is the deepest - **Cat Stevens**

I Want To Hold Your Hand - **The Beatles**

Have You Seen Your Mother, Baby,
Standing in the Shadow - **The Rolling Stones**

Into The Mystic - **Van Morrison**

If You're Going to San Francisco - **Scott McKenzie**

Love is like a cigarette, the bigger the drag,
the more you get - **'Stunted Sonnet' Adrian Mitchell**

The Eve of Destruction - **Barry McGuire**

I saw the best minds of my generation destroyed by madness, starving hysterical naked, dragging themselves through the negro streets at dawn looking for an angry fix, angelheaded hipsters burning for the ancient heavenly connection to the starry dynamo in the machinery of night....

- ' Howl' **Allen Ginsberg**

On The Road Again - **Canned Heat**

Tell Me Lies About Vietnam - **Adrian Mitchell**

Tonight I'll be staying here with you - **Bob Dylan**

We've Gotta Get Out of This Place - **Spencer Davis Group**

Please Don't Let Me Be Misunderstood - **The Animals**

*Everybody's Got Something to Hide
                Except for Me & My Monkey* - **The Beatles**

While My Guitar Gently Weeps - **George Harrison**

Oh Lord Won't You Buy Me a Mercedes Benz - **Janis Joplin**

Homeward Bound - **Simon & Garfunkel**

Where Are We Now? - **David Bowie**

It's Over - **Roy Orbison**

Where Do You Go To My Lovely? - **Peter Starstedt**

I Was Lost in France - **Bonnie Tyler**

Get off of My Cloud - **The Rolling Stones**

I Won't Leave My Wooden Wife for you, Sugar
                              *- **United States of America***

She Talks To Rainbows - **The Ramones**

A Change is Going to Come - **Sam Cooke**

I'm Going Up Country - **Canned Heat**

Trippin' On a Hole In Your Paper Heart - **Stone Temple Pilots**

Yes, The River Knows - **The Doors**

There is a Light That Never Goes Out - **The Smiths**

Ride a White Swan - **T. Rex**

I Can't Make You Love Me - **Bonnie Raitt**

Riders On The Storm - **The Doors**

River Deep, Mountain High - **Ike & Tina Turner**

Listen, Do You Want to Know a Secret? - **The Beatles**

If Not For You - **Bob Dylan**

Printed in Great Britain
by Amazon